# Bound to Care

**Studies in Society**

Titles include:

# Bound to Care

V. A. Braithwaite

Allen & Unwin
Sydney Wellington London Boston

To Ben and Sari

First published in 1990
Allen & Unwin Australia Pty Ltd
An Unwin Hyman company
8 Napier Street, North Sydney, NSW 2059 Australia

Allen & Unwin New Zealand Limited
75 Ghuznee Street, Wellington, New Zealand

Unwin Hyman Limited
15-17 Broadwick Street, London W1V 1FP England

Unwin Hyman Inc.
8 Winchester Place, Winchester, Mass 01890 USA

National Library of Australia
Cataloguing-in-Publication entry:

Braithwaite, V. A. (Valerie A.), 1951–
   Bound to care.

   Bibliography.
   ISBN 0 04 442149 4.

   1. Caregivers — Australia — Psychology. 2. Caregivers —
   Australia — Job stress. 3. Medical care surveys —
   Australia. I. Title.

362.10230994

Library of Congress Catalogue Card Number: 89–046275

Set in 10/11 Times by SRM Production Services, Malaysia
Printed by Kim Hup Lee Printing, Singapore

# Contents

# List of Figures

# List of Tables

# Acknowledgements

Many books on caregiving have been written by those with personal experiences of providing care. For me that was not the case. In joining the Social Psychiatry Research Unit at the Australian National University, my interest lay in quite a different direction—I wanted to know how to age well. The beginnings of *Bound to Care* lay in a meeting I had with the Director of the Unit, Scott Henderson, in 1982 when he expressed enormous enthusiasm in someone from the Unit studying the problems of carers of frail aged people. I was sceptical. Reeling under the shock of a first baby, I wasn't at all sure I wanted to immerse myself in more caring, albeit from a research perspective. Nevertheless, I promised him I would think about the proposal and proceeded to talk to some women about caregiving. I remember the terror of those first interviews. One of the first carers I spoke to asked me what experience I had had of caregiving. I mumbled something of my grandmothers who had both died after long debilitating illnesses, but the fact was that I had not thought deeply about either of these experiences in the early stages of planning the project. Looking back, I think I was afraid to think of them. Bit by bit, I found the courage to recall the little I remembered of those days, enough to make me realise that caregiving was part of my past as it was likely to be part of my future, and that of those around me.

As I talked to more and more carers, I came to understand their difficulties, to share their pains, but most of all to admire their courage, not least of all the courage of those who were struggling to keep going. They saw themselves doing what they had to do, they took one day at a time as their emotional well-being see-sawed—they hoped yet they grieved, they loved yet they felt anger, they felt they were giving their all, yet they felt guilty. Their courage became my motivation to write this book. In the words of one carer, 'You've got my life there in that box. Make sure you make a good job of it!'

To all those carers who found the time to talk with me and share a piece of their lives, my most sincere thanks. Yours is a story that everyone should care about. I hope I have told it well.

I have many others to thank for helping me bring the lives of the carers I spoke to into my world of science. My thanks to Scott Henderson, not only for the enthusiasm he expressed for the project, but for the resources he made available to me while I was in his Unit. My gratitude also to the Woden Valley Hospital staff and the Community Nurses who helped me contact carers: Julie Munro-Ashman; Shirley Bazley; Jean Brichacek; Marilla Lenne and Hilary Lang. At the stage of collecting and analysing data, I was fortunate to have access to a wonderful group of secretaries and research assistants in the Social Psychiatry Research Unit. The questionnaires were ably typed by Karen Maxwell and Penny Evans. Margaret Goodchild and Jane Hutchinson were superb interviewers, providing me with a wealth of data to draw on. Their commitment and sensitivity ensured that I felt no more distant from their interviews than I did from my own. As I analysed data, I had the pleasure of working with Anna Pino who always greeted my 'one extra, but definitely last analysis' with indefatigable patience, good humour and a knowing look; and as I laboured over the first draft of the manuscript, Penny Evans quickly turned it into a typescript which looked so professional that it never failed to lift flagging spirits. As *Bound to Care* passed through all these stages, I had the benefit of sharing my ideas with the late Paul Duncan-Jones. Paul had the knack of always making problems seem far more surmountable. He invariably would offer me a new perspective on something I had been puzzling over for days and I always left his office thinking in a different and more productive way than I had been when I walked in.

As I moved to a new job with *Bound to Care* almost complete, the final stages were made far more palatable by a very supportive network of friends and colleagues. My thanks to Sid Sax; Diane Gibson; Alice Day; John Braithwaite; Phillip Pettit; Debbie Terry and Eileen McNally for their constructive comments on earlier drafts of the book; to Russell Darroch and Toni Makkai for launching me into the world of word-processing; to Robert Lynd-Stevenson for his computing assistance; to Dorothy Broom and Claire Williams for broadening my perspective on caregiving. Nor can I overlook the contribution of three very special friends whose work habits, like mine, led them to burn the midnight oil in the ANU Psychology Department. Their offerings of coffee and chocolate, their good humour and their considerable computing expertise saved me from despair on more than one occasion and made the writing of the never-ending story, as they affectionately came to call it, a sociable and happy experience.

Finally, my thanks to my family, all of whom will undoubtedly breathe a sigh of relief to see this book in print. As I sat at my desk absorbed in the lives of the caregivers I had interviewed, I couldn't help but notice the caring activities of my own family. As I look back, four snapshots come to mind—my mother's Sunday phone call always beginning with the question, 'Is the book finished yet?'; my husband reminding me that if only I'd look I'd see the light at the end of the tunnel; my son lecturing me on good eating habits and making me hot chocolate and peanut butter sandwiches as I sat glued to the computer; and my daughter teaching me that although academic goals cannot be accomplished through cuddles, the long haul is made so much more enjoyable because of them.

# 1 Caregiving burden — an increasing consideration

The prospect of becoming dependent on others for basic needs is regarded with trepidation by most of us. Dependency in adulthood threatens cherished values of self-respect and human dignity. The acquisition of skills and ultimately independence is followed with keen interest in our society, planned for with enthusiasm, and celebrated with pride. In contrast, the loss of such skills is rarely planned for, and at times dealt with in a patronising or embarrassed fashion. Yet dependency cannot be overlooked by those whose lives are so affected or by those who care about them. Supporting chronically ill, handicapped or frail aged people is a frontline of unpaid carers, usually female, assuming major responsibility for care. Not only are they a lifeline for those needing assistance, but the successful implementation of health care policy throughout the western world depends on their efforts. This book focuses on the unpaid carers and their needs.

Increasingly, in a bid to curb welfare expenditure, governments are favouring policies advocating community care over institutional care (House of Representatives Standing Committee on Expenditure, 1982; New South Wales Department of Health, 1983; Scull, 1985; Walker, 1982). Community care provides formal services to people while they continue to live at home, and at the same time harnesses the informal support provided by family, friends and neighbours. In general, this approach is seen to be more cost effective than placing people in long stay hospitals or residential care where support is provided primarily by paid staff (Greer & Mor, 1986; Rimmer, 1983; Wright et al., 1981).

The economic arguments for deinstitutionalisation have been given considerable impetus by the increasing costs of aged care. While the disabled are in a minority from childhood to old age, this proportion reaches its highest levels among older age groups (Australian Bureau of Statistics, 1982; Moroney, 1986). As the number of elderly people increases in relation to the rest of the population, provision of adequate care for those who are frail and disabled threatens to be increasingly costly (Kinnear & Graycar, 1982; Rossiter & Wicks, 1982; Sax, 1984; Wade & Hewer, 1983).

1

Reallocating resources from institutional to community care has been embraced by governments as the best option for meeting the demand while containing costs (Greenberg et al., 1980; House of Representatives Standing Committee on Expenditure, 1984; Walker, 1983).

Apart from its economic advantages, community care is attractive, psychologically and socially, for the disabled and their families. In providing necessary services, institutions invariably deprive individuals of their freedom, discourage independence in other spheres of life, and isolate residents from family, friends and 'life outside' (Collopy, 1988; Hendricks & Hendricks, 1977; Ronalds, 1989; Swain & Harrison, 1979). The vast majority of elderly people value their independence highly and are reluctant to leave their homes to be cared for elsewhere (Blau, 1973; Day, 1985; Hellebrandt, 1980; Kendig, 1986; Wenger, 1984). Fears of 'ending up' in a nursing home echo through our society. Research documents such concerns (Minichiello, 1986; Ronalds, 1989; Tobin & Lieberman, 1978) and our literature expresses the depth of anguish that some experience: 'I am not mad only old. I make this statement to give me courage ... I am in a concentration camp for the old, a place where people dump their parents or relatives exactly as though it were an ash can' (from *As we are now* by May Sarton, 1973, p. 9).

Negative attitudes to nursing homes are not restricted to those who harbour fears of impending dependency. Public scepticism about the quality of institutional life is never far below the surface, particularly in individualistically-oriented societies such as our own. Reports by relatives of residents receiving poor food, inappropriate medication, over-sedation, physical and emotional neglect, and physical violence are not uncommon (Cartwright et al., 1973; Ronalds, 1989; Social Welfare Action Group, 1982). Accompanying this uncertainty about institutional care is a commitment to the notion of family care. Confidence in the family as the ideal provider of care is evident in social welfare policies (Moroney, 1986; New South Wales Parliament, 1982; O'Neill, 1983) and in the debates which have raged in the past regarding working mothers, child care centres, and even kindergartens (Burns & Goodnow, 1979).

Until relatively recently, however, we failed to appreciate the degree to which commitment to the ideal of family care extended beyond our children to include adult dependent relatives. The folk wisdom has been that the modern nuclear family has cut itself off from the extended family, particularly frail elderly relatives. Being so bound up in their own lives, families today are assumed to regard any dependent elderly relative as a nuisance to be dumped in a home at the first opportunity. Yet research in a number of countries over the past decade has shown consistently that such a practice is the exception, not the rule. Contrary to popular mythology, the family's sense of responsibility for care of frail elderly people is alive and well (Cicirelli, 1981; Fadel-Girgis, 1983; Gibson, 1984; Howe, 1979; Maeda, 1983; Shanas, 1979a; Tobin & Kulys, 1981).

Although elderly parents and their children tend not to live in the same premises in western society, a modified extended family system operates. 'Intimacy at a distance', a term coined by Rosenmayr and Köckeis (1963), captures the essence of the dominant living arrangement for elderly people and their families for the last quarter of a century. Parents and children have separate dwellings, but they tend to live in the same geographical area (Rowland, 1986; Shanas & Hauser, 1974). Shanas (1979a) described this as a practice which allows aged persons to maintain their independence and children their privacy. Visits and contacts between these households remain high, and when illness occurs the family provides the major support (Litwak, 1960; Sussman, 1965; Uzoka, 1979). Brody (1977) has pointed out how seriously families take their responsibilities: 'Studies of the paths leading to institutional care have shown that placing an elderly relative is the last, rather than first resort of families. In general, they have exhausted all other alternatives, endured severe personal, social and economic stress in the process, and made the final decision with the utmost reluctance.'

Thus, fiscal constraints, preservation of individual rights, and family ties all point to community care as the best available option for disabled people and their families. In recent years, however, the implementation of community care policies has come under close scrutiny and questions have been raised about who is bearing the costs.

Recipients of community care are by no means a homogeneous group. At one end of the spectrum are men and women who maintain a degree of independent living with limited assistance from formal services such as Meals on Wheels and Home Help and occasional favours from family and friends. At the other end of the spectrum are the more dependent who survive in the community through heavy reliance on assistance, most commonly provided by one person known as the primary carer or caregiver. For this group, institutionalisation is prevented only by the availability of that person—usually a family member and usually female (Brody, 1978; Kendig et al., 1983; Shanas, 1979b; Stephens & Christianson, 1986; Tobin & Kulys, 1981).

This well-documented pattern of caregiving has led Walker (1983) to conclude that in the rhetoric of policy initiatives on care, 'both "community" and "family" are euphemisms for female kin' (p. 114). The finding that care, which in theory should be shared, is falling disproportionately on the shoulders of women becomes increasingly disturbing when the costs are looked at. Direct costs, that is, extra expenses incurred through caring include additional heating, special foodstuffs, medical supplies and equipment, and wear and tear on clothes and furniture (Baldwin, 1976; Hyman, 1977; Pilling, 1981). Indirect costs refer to foregone earnings—carers may have to reduce their hours of work, be selective about the type of work they take on, turn down promotions, or even give up work altogether (Chetwynd, 1983; Equal Opportunities Commission, 1982; Rimmer, 1983; Stone et al., 1987). Further costs may be incurred through time out of the labour market. Re-entry into the workforce may be difficult and carers are likely to be disadvantaged in terms of occupational pension schemes (Abel, 1987; Rimmer, 1983). Last but not least caring may cost carers dearly in terms of their social and emotional well-being (Equal Opportunities Commission, 1980; Jones & Vetter, 1984). These costs are increasingly being referred to in the literature as the 'burden' of the carer.

The issue of sacrifice can be dealt with at two levels of analysis. The first is societal, the key questions being 1) why does the burden of care fall disproportionately on the shoulders of women? 2) what are the consequences of this for women and men? and 3) how can the imbalance be corrected in the community care system? Feminist literature has begun to address all these questions. Central to such analyses is the notion that caring as unpaid work locks the identity of women into the family, makes women economically dependent on men and so reproduces patriarchy with all its inequities and inefficiencies (Finch & Groves, 1980, 1982; Graham, 1983; Walker, 1983).

The second level of analysis examines caring sacrifice at the individual level, the key questions being 1) what is the burden that carers experience? 2) how does it come about? and 3) how can the experience of burden be alleviated? The central approach here has been to document the financial, social and emotional problems that carers perceive themselves and their families as having when they assume care of a frail elderly person (Jones & Vetter, 1984; Stephens & Christianson, 1986; Zarit, Reever & Bach-Peterson, 1980; Rossiter, Kinnear & Graycar, 1984).

As research findings have accumulated on the issue of caregiving burden, the impetus for understanding the nature of this stress, particularly in caregivers of the elderly, has also increased. Burden is widely accepted as a major consideration in the family's decision to institutionalise frail elderly relatives (Isaacs, 1971; Morycz, 1985; Stephens & Christianson, 1986). Burden is believed to underlie physical and mental illness in a substantial proportion of caregivers (Equal Opportunities Commission, 1980; Goldman & Luchins, 1984; Grad & Sainsbury, 1963, 1968). Burden is regarded as placing the well-being of frail elderly persons in jeopardy (Dunkle, 1985), in extreme cases resulting in mistreatment and abuse (Hudson, 1986; Kosberg & Cairl, 1986; Lau & Kosberg, 1979). Burden, therefore, has emerged as an issue of some significance for policy makers, health and welfare workers, and families. It will also be a key issue in analysing the needs of caregivers in this book.

Although there is now a considerable body of literature documenting the demographic, social, and personal characteristics of caregivers, their lifestyle, and their difficulties (e.g. Cantor, 1983; Gilleard et al., 1984a; Jones & Vetter, 1984), a clear picture has not emerged of the specific factors that make caregiving more stressful for some than for others (Pearson et al., 1988). There is little doubt that the majority of carers care because they want to (Brody, 1981; Brody et al., 1983). For some, caregiving brings its own rewards even in the saddest circumstances: 'It would take one and a half hours to put him to bed each night. I couldn't do it in any less. When at last I gave him a goodnight kiss, he would always say to me, "Thank you for all you have done for me today". It was never automatic. Each time I knew he meant it. And I'd leave the room feeling ten feet tall.' For others, there are no compensations, just bitter memories of ruined lives: 'Our family life used to be happy. He was a good father. The change was so immense. One of the hardest things to manage was his lack of response—he wouldn't cooperate. He'd pull me over—blame me. I nursed a relative a few years back. He wasn't like that—he'd try to help. But not my husband. He didn't appreciate anything I did. I'm sure he would have responded better if he'd been somewhere else, if someone else had looked after him.'

Understanding the factors that allow some carers to tread their difficult path more positively than others is a major goal of this book. The identification of the circumstances which put carers at risk of burden is of paramount importance in targeting community programmes successfully to those in need of relief. So too is a greater appreciation of the notion of sharing care. While sharing offers a way to redress the current imbalance in who provides care and so achieve more equitable community care, it also may play a significant role in alleviating the burden of the carer.

# 2 Caregiving burden — what the literature tells us

Providing care for an aged and disabled spouse or relative has been accepted widely as an exhausting and harrowing experience, indeed a burden. This presumption has been based on a sizeable literature detailing the workload of carers and the sacrifices they have made. Yet burden is very much a subjective phenomenon. Burden means 'that which is borne with difficulty' (*Macquarie Dictionary*, 1982). Specific demands are met with differing degrees of ease by different people. Tasks which are problematic for one person may be quite inconsequential for another. Therefore, burden cannot be regarded as a universal caring phenomenon. Burden, like beauty, is very much in the eye of the beholder.

Yet the earliest and most popular practice in the literature has been to identify burden with particular events and activities (see Platt, 1985). Included are those consistently reported as difficult, such as the disruption of family life (Equal Opportunities Commission, 1980; Grad & Sainsbury, 1963; Robinson, 1983), as well as those which are not considered so difficult, such as urinary incontinence (Isaacs, 1971; Sanford, 1975). This approach seeks to objectify the burden concept. Whether or not caregivers regard the experience as a problem is irrelevant.

To distinguish what is presumed to be negative from the caregivers' feelings and evaluations, Hoenig and Hamilton (1968) used the terms 'objective burden' and 'subjective burden' respectively. In spite of the fact that the events and activities of caregiving appear to be only weakly related to the feelings which they arouse in caregivers (Hoenig & Hamilton, 1966; Montgomery et al., 1985; Thompson & Doll, 1982), the term burden has been retained to describe both the caregiving situation and the caregiver's reactions. Indeed, the distinction between the two types of burden, objective and subjective, has often been overlooked entirely, particularly at the measurement level (Montgomery et al., 1985).

This issue is not unique to this particular literature. The distinction between the occurrence of events and the interpretations that people make about them is pivotal in social science literature.[1] The critical question is whether key scientific concepts should be equated

6

with objective reality or subjective experience. Debates of this kind have raged for some time in relation to a range of concepts. Value theorists, for instance, have devoted considerable attention to whether values should be defined as properties of objects or as subjective person-centred phenomena (Levitin, 1973). Similarly, stress theorists have argued over whether stress should be defined in terms of environmental change or as the individual's reaction to this change (Dohrenwend et al., 1984; Fleming et al., 1984; Lazarus et al., 1985). Increasingly, subjective person-centred approaches in these fields have gained in popularity. The caregiving literature is no exception (Morycz, 1985; Pratt et al., 1985).

Relying heavily on the person-centred tradition, Poulshock and Deimling (1984) defined caregiving burden in terms of the distress arising from dealing with the carereceiver's debilities and behaviours. To be distinguished from burden are the concepts of impairment and impact. Impairment refers to the carereceiver's inability to perform activities of daily living, cognitive incapacity, or difficult and disruptive behaviour patterns. The effects of caregiving on family, social life, work, and employment constitute impact. This approach narrows the concept of burden considerably. It links burden with carers' perceptions, thereby avoiding the problem of labelling particular difficulties as burdensome for all carers. Its disadvantage, however, is that it makes no allowance for the caregivers' feelings about impact. The literature would suggest that distress arising from overload and divided loyalties is just as important as distress arising from debilities (Cantor, 1980; Dunkle, 1985; Horowitz, 1978).

One possible solution is to broaden Poulshock and Deimling's (1984) concept so that burden covers both distress in providing care to a person and distress at the impact that caregiving has on one's life. Such a compromise, however, reduces the clarity of the Poulshock and Deimling model. For instance, how does one distinguish objective impact from subjective impact? While it is possible to differentiate conceptually between the occurrence of role conflict on the one hand and distress over role conflict on the other, separating the two empirically is likely to be difficult for those involved. Even for an external observer, inferences about role conflict could not help but be influenced by observation of behaviour reflecting the carer's distress.

To resolve this dilemma, we should question whether there are any advantages in maintaining the objective–subjective dichotomy. Previous work has demonstrated little empirical relationship between the two. Standard definitions of burden make the notion of objective burden a contradiction in terms. Under such circumstances, there is little to be lost and much to be gained by setting aside the notion of objective burden. The central issue then becomes whether or not the subjective definition of burden as 'distress aroused by the impact on lifestyle and the dependant's debilities and behaviours' captures the essence of the concept. Reservations can best be explained by first examining some of the things that commonly upset caregivers.

Among the most frequently mentioned losses are financial and employment sacrifices, the loss of friends and the restriction of one's social life, giving up leisure activities, the loss of freedom and privacy, and the loss of sleep (Archbold, 1983; Barnes et al., 1981; Cartwright et al., 1973; Dunkle, 1985; Equal Opportunities Commission, 1980; Grad & Sainsbury, 1963, 1968; Jones & Vetter, 1984; Thompson & Haran, 1985). Disruption of household routine and family life has also been documented (Grad & Sainsbury, 1963, 1968), and Barnes et al., (1981) and Fengler and Goodrich (1979) report the difficulty for caregivers who must assume new roles. Considerable attention has also focused on the degree of handicap and disability in the carereceiver. Dangerous and demanding behaviour has been recorded as a major cause of carer upset (Grad & Sainsbury, 1963; Robinson & Thurnher, 1979; Sanford, 1975).

Yet most of these experiences are an integral part of caring in other areas of life as well. Take a new-born baby as an example. The same losses occur—one's social life is restricted, sleep is broken, work is often relinquished or compromised, savings are eroded, and freedom is lost. The same changes take place—the household is thrown into a state of chaos and family life is disrupted. An even greater level of dependency is handled with pride and affection, and rarely interpreted as burden. As the child grows, tantrums and other behaviours may cause annoyance and embarrassment, but parents tend to show remarkable acceptance, dismissing their children's anti-social activities as just a stage they all go through. Where then does the difference lie? What is the source of the burden in caring for elderly people or adults who are no longer able to care for themselves?

Burden is regarded as being most acute where caring does not follow the desired path, where it does not make things better, and where it accompanies losses rather than gains in the well-being of the recipient. Five types of crises for carers are considered to arise out of decline, crises which may have a deleterious effect on carer well-being—awareness of degeneration, unpredictability, time constraints, the caregiver-carereceiver relationship, and choice restrictions. These crises of decline are either absent or do not assume the same potency in normal child-rearing practice.

Our society puts great importance on independence and personal growth. Children mature and become independent, leaving parents with a sense of pride and accomplishment. Elderly people, on the other hand, are more likely to grow weaker with care, losing independence, their sense of self-worth, and sometimes even losing touch with reality, leaving caregivers with feelings of hopelessness and frustration (Archbold, 1983; Cantor, 1980; Barnes et al., 1981; Robinson & Thurnher, 1979; Strong, 1984). The difference is a difference of outcomes. The emotional involvement in child rearing is usually reinforcing, bringing happiness, security, and hope for a rewarding future. The elderly person's decline is painful to observe. Past memories exacerbate the loss, and the degeneration is a constant reminder of the inevitability of the even greater loss to come.

The second crisis, unpredictability, arises out of the first. Degeneration is not as predictable as maturation. As children grow, their development follows a well-known path. Parents watch for and mark off the milestones: smiling, sitting, and crawling in the first year; walking, talking, and feeding oneself in the second; and toilet training in the third. There is both knowledge that caregiving levels will systematically decrease and expectations for when developmental stages should be reached. In contrast, there are no comparable charts outlining the stages of de-development. Different diseases take different courses, the same disease affects different people in different ways, and one disease can affect each person differently from one day to the next. For carers of older adults the future is often unpredictable (Barnes et al., 1981). They do not know what will be required of them tomorrow, let alone in a year, and they do not know for how long they will need to give care.

The third crisis of decline, time constraints, affects caregivers at two levels. First, as dependency increases, caregiving falls on the shoulders of one particular person. Rarely is it a shared responsibility (Brody, 1981, 1985). In contrast, sharing of care is institutionalised in normal child-rearing situations through schooling, kindergartens and play groups, and provided informally either through baby-sitting or going to a friend's house to play or stay over. Carers of those who are losing rather than acquiring skills do not have such a range of alternatives available, have no tradition of such use to guide them, and therefore, are less likely to have relief from caregiving.

At a second level, time constraints are likely to be exacerbated by the carer's life stage. Where parent care is provided, the caregiver is likely to be a daughter with a family of her own and possibly employment outside the home (Brody, 1981; Treas, 1977). To provide for an elderly person at such a time is a distraction from the caregiver's already time-consuming commitments. It is not surprising that the literature is replete with reports of role overload and conflict for carers (Cantor, 1980; Equal Opportunities Commission, 1980; Montgomery et al., 1985).

The social and emotional relationship between adult caregiver and adult carereceiver, the fourth crisis, is likely to be less stable than that between parents and young children. Young children are expected to love and obey their parents, and parents are expected to love, teach, and protect their children. No such guidelines govern care of an older adult. Indeed, old norms may need to be reversed when care is required. Once a family member has accepted responsibility to care, no assurances can be given about whether or not the caregiver and carereceiver will get along in their new dependency relationship. No safeguards exist against one dominating the life of the other, and the potential for conflict is increased. This kind of conflict is well recognised in our society, featuring prominently in comedy sketches (particularly about mothers-in-law) and television programmes across the world (e.g. 'Fresh Fields' in Britain, 'Mother and Son' in Australia, and 'Sanford and Son' in the United States). While expectations of interpersonal difficulties are widespread in relation to aged care, few parents-to-be would contemplate conflict with their new born infant. Power relations are clearly defined in this caring context.

Finally, lack of choice is a far more important issue in caring for an older adult than in rearing a child. Today there is choice in whether to or when to become parents. Adults can decide to avoid these responsibilities or take them on at a time which suits them. In contrast, caregivers to the elderly are responding to the need for help in another. Given the strength of family ties, caregivers have little choice but to give and give immediately (Brody et al., 1983; Shanas, 1979a; Sussman, 1965). In so doing, they may be forced to put aside other plans, forego activities and even undertake tasks which are beyond their capability.

Life stage, already mentioned as an important factor influencing time constraints, can also be used to illustrate caregivers' lack of choice. While there is a right time to care for children, there really is no right time to care for older adults. Caring for a frail elderly person while caring for children is an option that few would like to have forced upon them. Where care for an elderly person follows care for children, other plans and aspirations may be jeopardised. Women re-entering the workforce or wishing to pursue their careers may be frustrated by new caregiving responsibilities. Alternatively, caregivers may see themselves forsaking their golden years—their time to reap the rewards of their labours (Crossman et al., 1981; Robinson & Thurnher, 1979; Treas, 1977). The post-child-rearing stage of life promises freedom, which, when coupled with retirement from the workforce, is the socially sanctioned time for self-indulgence and enjoyment of life to the full. Again, caring for an elderly person interferes with the achievement of these goals.

Where caregiving is experienced even later in life, a new difficulty arises. The carer's own ageing is likely to set limits on just what can and cannot be done. As the caregiver's well-being fluctuates, so too does the capacity to meet the needs of the carereceiver (Cantor, 1983; Crossman et al., 1981; Soldo & Myllyluoma, 1983).

While physical capacity to care is likely to be age related, the problem is not confined to older carers. Physical strength is far more likely to be required in administering care to an adult than to a child. For carers who are physically unable to measure up to the demands of lifting and moving their dependant, lack of choice may have very serious consequences for their own well-being.

The five crises of decline—awareness of degeneration, unpredictability, time constraints, the caregiver-carereceiver relationship, and choice restriction—describe the major differences between child rearing and aged caring. What one actually gives to an ageing person is really quite similar to what one gives to a child. Burden does not lie in the giving of assistance. What is different in the two types of care is willingness and capacity to give. Both are reduced when care is required for an elderly relative. Awareness of decline restricts the pleasure associated with caregiving and threatens the caregiver's own sense of security. Perceptions of threat are central to the notion of burden. Yet this was not the major focus of the definition offered earlier. Burden was conceptualised in terms of the distress aroused by the impact on lifestyle and the dependant's debilities and behaviours.

Although distress is likely to be associated with threat, the concepts are not synonymous. Stress theorists such as Lazarus et al. (1985) differentiate between the way in which an individual appraises an event and the emotional reaction that person has to the event. A person may perceive an event as threatening, but if appropriate coping strategies are used, distress may be minimised, if not avoided.

By defining burden in terms of threat, notions of assessing caregiver activity objectively or emotional distress subjectively are both being rejected. The former denies the subjective nature of the construct. The latter satisfies the subjective criterion, but is more removed from the caregiving context than may be desirable. Feelings of upset are nebulous, they can spill over from other walks of life, and they are more readily and forcefully expressed by some than by others. Burden as threat involves subjective evaluation, but requires caregivers to assess their situation rather than vent their feelings. In this way, the more emotionally volatile caregivers do not have sole claim to the notion of burden. Those who are highly restrained emotionally may be burdened as well.

## A definition of burden

Burden is defined as the caregiver's perception of the extent to which the meeting of caregiving demands threatens satisfaction of the caregiver's basic needs. The definition has three key elements. First, it specifies that carers are the informants on the degree to which caregiving threatens need satisfaction. Second, it restricts the threat to the caregiving context. Third, it defines the target of the threat as basic needs.

### Defining basic needs

Need is defined as 'the lack of something which, if present, would tend to further the welfare of the . . . [individual]' (English & English, 1958). The point of departure for identifying 'the something' is Maslow's (1954, 1962) breakdown of types of needs. Maslow identified two broad categories of needs — basic needs and metaneeds. Basic needs are deficiency needs in that they are experienced by the individual as annoying states of which he or she wants to be rid. Satisfaction of the need reduces discomfort. Failure to satisfy can breed illness. In Maslow's (1962) words, deficiency needs are 'empty holes, so to speak, which must be filled up for health's sake . . .' (p. 21). Maslow enumerated four basic needs — physiological needs, safety needs, belongingness and love needs, and esteem needs. Metaneeds, in contrast, do not create annoying or unpleasant states and provide the impetus for growth and personal development.

Burden is concerned with deprivation of basic needs, not metaneeds. Restricting the definition in this way strengthens the burden concept from both a scientific and policy perspective. The importance of basic needs is widely recognised by psychological theorists other than Maslow (see Fromm, 1941; Murray, 1938). Less consensus surrounds the concept of metaneeds. Basic needs assume priority over metaneeds because, according to Maslow, they need to be satisfied before growth can take place and because deprivation is a cause of illness. The second proposition is well supported in the stress literature. Insufficient sustenance and rest, disruption, social isolation, loss of freedom, and loss of self-respect have all been shown to jeopardise well-being (Bettelheim, 1960; Kleitman, 1963; Miller & Seligman, 1975; Roth & Kubal, 1975; Schachter, 1959). Further, from a social policy viewpoint, modern welfare states generally accept the responsibility for assisting those suffering special circumstances of deprivation (including caregivers) to meet basic needs. Where deprivation threatens health, governments do have a vested interest in providing relief. Where deprivation threatens one of society's most cherished institutions, the family, governments are willing to consider assistance.

Burden as basic need frustration offers a number of other advantages of an ethical as well as scholarly nature. Attempts to link burden with disabilities in the carereceiver or the emotional reactions of the caregiver create ethical dilemmas for researchers. To tie burden to disabilities reinforces the view of the carereceiver as the burden. The alternative practice of associating burden with the caregiver's feelings of distress gives rise to evaluations of caregivers as weak or inept. Both approaches are invitations to allocate blame and are guilt-inducing—those being cared for feel guilty about being a burden, whereas those providing care experience guilt for not having sufficient strength and endurance. The proposed definition purports that burden is not caused by the receiver or the provider of care, but arises from the interaction between the two. The burden is created by the conflict between the demands of one and the needs of the other. Burden stems from poor person–environment fit; it is not an individualistic variable but an interactive one.

Conceptualising burden in this way offers further insight into why the caregiving situation may be difficult. Models of person–environment fit have been popular in examining worker satisfaction. In extending the model to unpaid carers, burden is not a surprising phenomenon. For both paid workers and unpaid carers, successful outcomes would be predicted if the attributes, skills, and needs of the person can be matched with the demands of the situation. To achieve this end, employers choose employees from a pool of applicants and prospective employees shop around for a job to their liking. In contrast, the frail elderly turn to their families (Brody et al., 1978; Shanas, 1979a, 1979b). The pool of applicants in this case is a very restricted captive sample and the pressure on them to accept the position is enormous, even if they deem themselves unsuitable.

*Is burden a problem?*

Available evidence suggests that the risk of poor person–environment fit in voluntary home care situations is high. There is more anxiety and depression among caregivers (Gilleard, 1984a; Grad & Sainsbury, 1968; Jones & Vetter, 1984; Thompson & Haran, 1985) and lower life satisfaction (Fengler & Goodrich, 1979; George & Gwyther, 1986; Robinson & Thurnher, 1979). Furthermore, nursing homes are flourishing in spite of high costs and tight government controls. Caregivers often have their elderly relatives' names on waiting lists, sometimes with the intention of accepting a bed, other times as a back-up in the event that they can no longer care (Gray & Lazarus, 1988; Howe, 1981). Community demand for nursing homes suggests that burden may be a serious problem.

## Assumptions and goals of this study

Before outlining the assumptions and goals of this study, mention should be made of some important issues it does not address. First, the focus is on the carer's basic need frustration, an experience I have labelled burden. But the concept of frustration of basic needs can be applied equally well to the carereceiver. From this perspective, a more appropriate label might be 'neglect'. We should bear in mind that caregiver burden and carereceiver neglect are related concepts, often manifestations of the same interaction (Kosberg & Cairl, 1986). If the well-being of one member of the partnership is adversely affected, the well-being of the other is likely to suffer.

Second, in conducting this study, the vast majority of carers encountered were caring for older family members. Thus, in the chapters that follow, aged care, family care, community care, and caring units are used interchangeably. Care does take place outside families, however, and care is given to the young as well as to the old. The emphasis of this book does not imply that the needs of these other groups are any less important. The ideas presented here can be extended to better appreciate the plight of gay couples where one partner has AIDS, of families in which a child is terminally ill, or of partners or parents of permanently disabled accident victims.

In planning the present study, five assumptions were made about the nature of caregiving burden:

1 Burden does not vary randomly, but varies systematically with specific features of the caregiving situation.
2 Burden can be meaningfully examined across caregivers who differ on age, gender, social class, relationship to the carereceiver, and residential status, and across carereceivers who differ on gender, age (providing they are adults), disability and illness.
3 Caregivers are able to report on the extent to which caregiving frustrates the fulfilment of basic needs, once these needs are defined for them.
4 Although caregivers are aware of their frustrations, they are not necessarily able to identify the specific features of home care which bring about these states. Traditionally, research on caregiving has relied heavily on caregivers' introspective accounts of the reasons for their distress and despair. As valuable as such reports are, the methodology has limitations. Under stressful and threatening circumstances, individuals are not always able to report accurately the factors underlying their distress and frustration (Cannell & Kahn, 1968; Moser & Kalton, 1971). Repression, denial, and socially desirable responding may hinder our understanding of the determinants of burden.

5 Following from assumption 4, statistical methods provide an alternative, complementary, and perhaps a more useful means of examining the relationship between specific features of home care and perceptions of burden.

With these assumptions in mind, five research goals were derived to guide the study. First and foremost was the task of assessing burden. Given that the present definition differed significantly from the conceptualisations of others, a special measure of burden was developed. Standard measures of mental health and psychological well-being were added, not only to establish the validity of the present measure of burden, but also to bridge the gap between this and other work in the field. Mental health and well-being measures have been used widely (Fengler & Goodrich, 1979; Gilhooly, 1984; Gilleard, 1984a; Grad & Sainsbury, 1968; Jones & Vetter, 1984).

The second goal was derived from assumption 3. If carers are not necessarily able to identify the specific features of caregiving which lead to burden and poor mental health, potential risk factors should be assessed independently and their statistical relationship to burden examined. At this point, practical constraints imposed a choice between gaining information on a lot of risk factors at one point in time or focusing on a smaller set which could be assessed with outcome measures at two points in time. With neither established theory nor data to narrow the set of potential risk factors, the first alternative was favoured. Thus, this study serves to identify the aspects of caregiving that are most strongly linked to burden, and does not demonstrate that they cause burden. Nevertheless, the study does propose a causal model for future investigation.

Although caregiving burden is assumed to be relevant to the experiences of different demographic groups, the levels of burden may differ from one to another. The third goal of this study, therefore, is to compare the caregiving experience across different demographic groups. Of particular interest are the variables of gender and whether care is being provided to a parent or spouse. Attention is increasingly being given to differences between male and female caregivers (Noelker & Wallace, 1985; Stone et al, 1987; Ungerson, 1987), one inference being that men are not as committed to the task as women. The spouse- or parent-caring situation is considered important on theoretical grounds, since the crises of decline, the proposed precursors of burden, are likely to affect these two groups differently. Other demographic variables considered are the caregiver's age, the carereceiver's age and gender, and the residential arrangement. The sample of caregivers was too homogeneous in terms of ethnicity to allow comparisons on this characteristic.

The fourth goal is to examine empirically the importance of so-called objective indices of burden. The characteristics which have been excluded from the present definition of burden and which others have included under the objective burden rubric are relegated to the role of independent variables in this study. Their importance compared with that of other predictors will be evaluated empirically.

Finally, a study of this kind should have policy implications for how governments are approaching the difficult problem of long-term care. Family care has found its way into the rhetoric of politicians as well as into government policy as a cost-efficient solution to aged care. The research community for some time now has questioned how cost efficient this strategy is. As governments are forced to confront the hidden costs, ways of reducing family burden will be sought and implemented. Some of these are already in place — day care, respite care, support groups, community nursing services and meal services. This study, through analysing and comparing the importance of a range of factors which have been thought to increase caregiving burden, can provide valuable insights into the directions in which we are now heading and perhaps suggest new approaches to relieving the burden of family caregivers.

# 3  Developing a research model

The approach of this study is to measure caregiving burden and its presumed contributing factors and statistically examine the importance of these factors, individually and collectively, as predictors of burden. The paradigm used is a modification of the dominant stress paradigm, of which a brief review will be useful here. Environmental stressors, life events, chronic life strains or daily hassles provoke physical and mental illness in some and not in others, leading to interest in factors which might intervene or moderate the relationship between the stressor on the one hand and the experience of stress on the other. These factors have been referred to variously as buffers, resistance resources, and vulnerability factors. Coping strategies, appraisal of an event as a challenge, a threat or a loss, self-esteem, mastery, hardiness and social support are variables which have received considerable attention as explanations for why the experience of an environmental stressor is inconsequential for some and traumatic for others (Brown & Harris, 1978; Dohrenwend & Dohrenwend, 1980; Fleming et al., 1984; Folkman & Lazarus, 1980; Holahan & Moos, 1985; Kaplan et al., 1983; Kobasa, 1979; Kobasa et al., 1981; Kobasa et al., 1985; Lazarus et al., 1985; Menaghan, 1982; Pearlin & Schooler, 1978; Pearlin et al., 1981; Wheaton, 1983).

The notion that personal and social resources can intervene or modify the relationship between an event and a person's reaction to that event has met with wide acceptance. Less is known, however, of the circumstances in which they perform these roles. In a number of studies, these factors have had a direct and independent influence on the level of stress experienced, and there has been little evidence of them assuming a protective or jeopardising role between the environmental stressor and the individual's stress reaction (see Billings & Moos, 1984; Kaplan et al., 1983; Kobasa et al., 1981; Shinn et al., 1984).

Clearly, caring for a person who is frail or ill is one kind of environmental stressor and such factors as coping skills, personality and social support must be considered as likely determinants of who will adapt successfully to the experience and who will not. Trans-

17

posing this paradigm directly to the caring situation, however, does not provide an optimal basis for understanding burden. Burden, as defined here, cannot be equated with a stress reaction, although the proposed measures of mental well-being would fulfil this function. Burden is best likened to the stress theorists' notion of the appraisal of an event. In this case, burden refers to a particular kind of appraisal: the appraisal that the event is threatening to basic needs. Our concern is in what leads to such an appraisal.

**The research model**

Three types of variables were considered important in developing a model of caregiving burden. Caregiving itself was not a variable since everyone interviewed was currently engaged in this activity. Regular caregiving demands, however, were expected to vary from one person to the next. Level of demand or workload could be regarded as an environmental stressor affecting the amount of threat carers perceived when faced with caregiving.

The second group of variables to be included in the model were personal, social or material resources. Variables were included if they had the potential for limiting the threat or harm which could result from caregiving. Of interest in this study were coping strategies, personal disposition, and physical well-being. Burden was expected to be least among those who dealt effectively with caregiving problems, who had a positive view of themselves and their ability to overcome difficulties, who were personally suited to the task, and who were physically capable of caregiving.

Social and material resources referred to outside conditions which could keep burden at bay. Informal support from family and friends and formal support from professionals were expected to fill some of the 'holes' in basic needs created by caregiving. Financial well-being was expected to fill others.

The third set of variables to feature in the model of caregiving burden did not have a counterpart in the stress literature. They are best conceptualised as critical components of the environmental stressor, caregiving. These variables were the crises of decline outlined in the previous chapter. The expectation is that the more extreme the crises for caregivers, the greater will be their burden. Thus, high burden is likely to be experienced when the carereceiver is seen to have deteriorated substantially, when caregiving demands have been unpredictable, when time constraints are great, when the relationship between caregiver and carereceiver is strained, and when carers have little choice about whether or not they will provide care.

All three types of variables were hypothesised as having a direct effect on burden. That is to say, burden should be high if the workload was high, if the resources were low, or if the crises of decline were extreme[1]. A detailed model of caregiving burden is presented in Table 3.1.

**Table 3.1  Predictors of caregiving burden**

Workload
    Task-oriented demands
    (daily activities, personal care, supervision, decision-making)
    Social-emotional demands
    (emotional and social support, maintaining social networks)
Resources
    Coping strategies
    Personality
    (self-esteem, mastery, emotionality, interest in others, activity)
    Health
    Social
    (availability of social interaction, informal and formal assistance, awareness of
    support)
    Material
    (financial well-being)
Crises of decline
    Awareness of degeneration
    Unpredictability
    Time constraints
    Caregiver–carereceiver relationship
    Choice restriction

## The workload variables

Workload refers to the activities in which carers engage and the responsibilities which they accept in order to promote the physical and mental well-being of their dependants. The work of the carer can be broken down into two broad categories, that which is task-oriented and primarily concerned with promoting physical well-being, and that which has a social-emotional focus, the major goal being to preserve mental health and quality of life.

### Task-oriented demands

Task-oriented demands involve the provision of services and as such encompass the more visible aspects of caregiving. Providing or organising assistance with daily activities and personal care fall into this category. Also included are the somewhat less obvious though unrelenting responsibilities of supervision and help with decision-making.

*Daily activities and personal care*: Providing assistance with shopping, dressing, washing, feeding, and transfers is generally tolerated well by caregivers (Gilleard et al., 1984a; Jones & Vetter, 1984; Sanford, 1975). Even urinary incontinence appears to be accepted by the majority (Gilleard et al., 1984a; Isaacs, 1971; Sanford, 1975; Wheatley, 1979), though faecal incontinence has been reported as causing greater carer distress (Sanford, 1975; Wheatley, 1979).

Tolerance of such tasks by the majority of caregivers does not preclude the possibility that the minority who do complain are the ones most likely to experience burden. This does not appear to be the case. Studies investigating the relationship between instrumental support and carer distress have produced few significant findings (Cantor, 1983; Fengler & Goodrich, 1979; Gilhooly, 1984; Greene et al., 1982; Jenkins et al., 1985; Montgomery et al., 1985; Pagel et al., 1985; Poulshock & Deimling, 1984; Zarit et al., 1980).

From the stress paradigm perspective, this is somewhat surprising. Additional demands would be expected to create stress and difficulties of adjustment. The finding is not so surprising, however, from the viewpoint of the burden analysis offered in the previous chapter. The instrumental tasks of caring for children and older adults are very similar and women are the major providers of care to both groups. If women incorporate aged-care tasks automatically into their daily routine the increased physical demands may go unnoticed. They would be doing more of the same thing.

One notable exception to the absence of significant findings in relation to workload is Morycz' (1985) study of caregivers of Alzheimer sufferers. Morycz found that the number of tasks performed for the carereceiver was significantly correlated with burden. Morycz' burden index, however, differed from those used in the above studies in that measures of distress were combined with measures of impact on lifestyle. Where need for assistance has been related to impact, consistent positive relationships have emerged (Cantor, 1983; Greene et al., 1982; Montgomery et al., 1985; Poulshock & Deimling, 1984). The need for greater assistance appears to restrict the carer's social life, family life, leisure activities, and work.

It must be remembered that the present definition of burden focuses on the frustration of basic needs, not on distress. While impact and basic need frustration are not identical, they are likely to be related. For this reason, instrumental tasks may be important in understanding burden and will be retained in the model in Table 3.1.

*Supervision*: Some elderly adults participate in daily activities and care for themselves for the most part, but they only do so safely if someone keeps a watchful eye on them—checks medication, guards against falls in the bath or toilet, and so on. For the cognitively impaired, an even higher level of supervision is often demanded to avoid accidents and prevent wandering (Mace & Rabins, 1981). Supervision, a more passive, yet more constant aspect of the workload than service provision, appears to be stressful for carers. Nissel (1984) has pointed out that supervisory responsibilities often impose the most constraints on other activities. Certainly the caregivers in the Robinson and Thurnher (1979), Gilleard et al. (1984a), and Chenoweth and Spencer (1986) studies emphasised the problems of confinement and not being able to leave the carereceiver for an hour or more. In comparing caregivers under high strain with those who were not, Isaacs (1971) concluded that constant supervision induced greater stress than performing specific tasks. Morycz (1985) also obtained a significant correlation between supervisory activities and his combined impact-stress index. Supervision shows every indication of being an important factor in explaining burden.

*Decision-making*: Related to supervision is the little studied issue of decision-making. Caring workload may involve accepting the responsibility for the well-being of another to the point of making decisions on his or her behalf, decisions which adults normally make for themselves (Golodetz et al., 1969; Mace & Rabins, 1981). Seeking medical attention for the carereceiver is one such example, but other decisions are made on a daily basis to provide structure to the day and maintain physical well-being. Professionals have observed the difficulty of assuming this role, particularly among spouses (Barnes et al., 1981), and caregivers have voiced uneasiness about this aspect of their workload (Horowitz, 1978). Horowitz, in analysing the benefits of support services to caregivers, concluded that bearing responsibility for the welfare of another is far more onerous than the physical rigours of providing care.

## Social-emotional demands

Work of a social-emotional kind is perhaps the least obvious aspect of caregiving and so fares particularly badly in the general devaluation of unpaid work (Daniels, 1987). Some carers even question whether it should be termed work, holding the view that 'finding time for a chat and a cup of tea is just being a decent human being'. Yet for carers, time is a scarce resource, and caregiving activities which take up time, regardless of how pleasant or unpleasant they are, should be taken into account in considering caregiving workload. Carers meet the social and emotional needs of their dependants on two fronts. First, they are likely to be called upon to provide support when the carereceiver is in pain, frightened, worried, lonely or depressed. Second, carers often play an active role in encouraging and helping carereceivers maintain their own social networks.

*Social and emotional support*: Nissel's (1984) time diaries and Stephens and Christianson's (1986) data on caregiving activities provide evidence of carers' involvement in activities of this kind. Cantor (1979, 1980) and Robinson and Thurnher (1979) have directed attention to the time-consuming nature of providing social and emotional support, which, according to Robinson and Thurnher, assumes greater importance for female than male carers.

Little is known about the effects on caregivers of providing emotional and social support. Focusing on female care providers, Belle (1982) has postulated that giving support, particularly when one is not receiving any, has serious consequences for health. Looking at the broader question of social relationships, Rook (1984) has reported that well-being can be adversely affected if one perceives relationships as entailing costs rather than rewards. Providing social and emotional support, therefore, may contribute to burden not only because of the time it consumes, but also because it can threaten well-being directly under certain circumstances.

*Maintaining the carereceiver's social network*: This second aspect of the social and emotional work of caregivers was recognised during some preliminary interviews which were conducted in preparation for the major study. Carers had accepted responsibility for ensuring that the social relationships of the carereceiver were preserved, that new acquaintances were made, and that interests were pursued. Sometimes this took the form of encouragement to write or phone people, sometimes invitations to visit, and other times transportation to events of interest. While this facet of caregiving is clearly part of the workload of carers, its importance has yet to be examined systematically.

### Resource variables

#### Coping strategies

When difficulties are encountered, people use coping strategies to avoid being harmed. A widely drawn distinction in the stress literature is between strategies which are problem-focused and those which are emotion-focused. A problem-focused approach would involve strategies designed to manage the difficulty and get the problem under control. An emotion-focused response, on the other hand, would be typified by ignoring the difficult situation and concentrating instead on accompanying feelings of distress. The coping strategies which people use and use effectively depend to a considerable degree on the situation (Folkman & Lazarus, 1980; McCrae, 1984; Pearlin & Schooler, 1978; Wheaton, 1983). There does seem to be a tendency, however, for effective strategies to fall into the problem-focused category more often than the emotion-focused category (Anderson, 1977; Billings & Moos, 1981, 1984; Colletta & Gregg, 1981; Felton & Revenson, 1984; Terry, 1989), and for avoidance strategies to be associated with high levels of stress (Holahan & Moos, 1985; Kobasa, 1982; Menaghan, 1982; Pearlin & Schooler, 1978).

In a study of the relationship between coping strategies and caregiving burden, Pratt et al. (1985) have reported results which are consistent with this pattern. Strategies oriented to resolving the difficulty or seeing the problem from a different perspective appeared to be effective coping strategies for carers. Avoidance responses were maladaptive.

A somewhat different viewpoint has been put forward by Strong (1984). Strong argues that acceptance and passivity may be adaptive coping responses for carers. After all, there is little that anyone can do when dealing with an incurable degenerative disease. Studies of the coping strategies of patients with incurable diseases suggest that there may be short-term benefits in denying their illness (Ell, 1985; Levine & Zigler, 1975). When illness is beyond their control, such strategies prevent patients from being overwhelmed by their predicament. Such an analysis may be just as applicable to caregivers. One might question, however, the long-term benefits of such an approach. While the disease may be uncontrollable, other aspects of caregiving such as the relief of symptoms and quality of life may well be controllable. Avoidance and denial of the illness may preclude the use of active and effective coping strategies in these related areas.

The traditional way of thinking about the operation of coping strategies is as part of a chain: A threat is perceived and a coping response is made, which if effective reduces feelings of distress and facilitates adaptation. From this perspective, coping is a consequence rather than a cause of burden.

Yet coping cannot be dismissed so readily as a precursor of burden in the caregiving context. For carers, the source of stress continues over months or years. It is reasonable to assume that caregiving does not instantly threaten basic needs, rather the threat builds up over time (see Jenkins et al., 1985). If so, effective coping strategies may curtail perceptions of threat, while ineffective strategies may provoke them. Consequently, coping strategies will be looked at as predictors of burden as well as mediators between burden and mental well-being.

*Personality*

Some carers were expected to have personalities that lessened the likelihood of them perceiving caregiving as a threat. High self-esteem and a sense of mastery were two personality characteristics expected to influence perceptions of burden. Both have been linked consistently with successful adaptation to life's problems (Kobasa, 1979; Lazarus et al., 1985; Wheaton, 1983).

The importance of high self-esteem in enabling carers to cope with their difficulties is supported by the study of Crossman et al. (1981). Low self-esteem was associated with caregivers blaming themselves for the problems they were experiencing, rather than seeing the situation as difficult. Self-blame is destructive to well-being (Pagel et al., 1985), and is likely to leave the caregiver afraid and vulnerable when faced with new difficulties.

Mastery refers to the belief that a person is in control of his or her destiny and that one is capable of making choices which overcome difficulties. The expectation is that the greater one's sense of personal mastery, the lower the likelihood that caregiving is perceived as a threat to basic needs. Instead, it is likely to be seen as a challenge. A study by Levine et al. (1983) suggests that mastery is indeed beneficial to carers. Carers who were skilful in handling difficulties were more likely to see themselves as having control over the things that happened to them.

Nevertheless, a query should be raised concerning the wisdom of carers implementing their sense of mastery indiscriminately. Clearly, not all aspects of caregiving are within the control of the carer. Fleming et al. (1984) have pointed out that the effectiveness of a control-based approach to life's problems depends upon the individual being responsible for the outcomes. According to Folkman (1984), mistakenly appraising an uncontrollable event as controllable runs the risk of implementing coping strategies which will only lead to frustration. Thus, mastery may only be advantageous to the caregiver when combined with an appreciation of the limitations that the situation imposes.

Burden was also expected to be a greater problem for those who were easily frightened, angered or upset, characteristics which some have labelled as neuroticism, but which will be referred to here as emotionality. Relevant data on the emotionality hypothesis can be found in the stress literature. In their study of the impact of negative life-change events, Holahan and Moos (1985) reported that 'easy-going' people adapted with fewer signs of physical or psychological strain. Further support comes from studies which have shown neuroticism to be a strong predictor of stress symptoms (Costa & McCrae, 1980; Henderson et al., 1981).

Among caregivers of the frail aged, Cantor (1983) found that worry about the carereceiver was predictive of reports of strain. One interpretation of this finding is that caregiving is characterised by a relatively high incidence of things going wrong. Carers who tend to be emotional will be easily frightened and put off by these experiences. They will feel these mishaps more acutely, take longer to settle down after them, and in the process will use up a lot of energy which would be best reserved for meeting other ever pressing demands. Apart from sapping the limited energies of the carer, an emotional temperament may have adverse effects on the care-receiver. Carers' upset is likely to be communicated to the care-receiver, indirectly if not directly, resulting in insecurity and stress on both sides.

Two other personality characteristics were considered to enhance a person's suitability for the caregiving role — concern for and interest in others and having a lot of energy. The first hypothesis is derived from vocational-choice research, where one's social orientation, defined as a preference to be with people and to be involved in service and help to others, has been linked with career choices such as nursing, teaching, and social work (Robinson et al., 1969; Robinson & Shaver, 1973). For those whose interests lie in other areas (e.g. in economic, political or theoretical pursuits), caregiving may be an enormously frustrating and unsuccessful endeavour.

The second aspect of personality which was expected to ease the burden of caregiving was activity level. Descriptions of the caregiving role have repeatedly emphasised the load that is being carried and the number of things which have to be attended to in a single day. This theme is aptly captured by Mace and Rabins (1981) in the title of their book *The 36-hour Day*. The reserves of energy which caregivers have to meet the demands made upon them each day, seven days a week, 365 days a year will set limitations on how well they can achieve their goals.

All five personality characteristics are regarded as factors which may influence the perception of burden. Like coping strategies, however, three may have a role to play in determining whether or not a perceived threat to basic needs flows on to adversely affect mental health. Those carers with high self-esteem and a sense of mastery might be expected to deal with their perceptions of burden more effectively and avoid loss of general psychological well-being. Emotionality, however, should have the opposite effect. Those who are highly emotional would be less likely to contain their feelings of threat in the caregiving situation and their mental health would be more likely to suffer.

## Health

The problem of poor physical health has been well documented among caregivers (Equal Opportunities Commission, 1980; Grad & Sainsbury, 1963, 1968; Pratt et al., 1985) and its adverse effect on the capacity to continue caring is widely recognised (Mace & Rabins,

1981; Storandt, 1983). The issue has been seen as particularly important in spouse caregiving situations because of the increasing age of the care provider (Cantor, 1983; Crossman et al., 1981; Noelker & Wallace, 1985; Soldo & Myllyluoma, 1983).

In spite of the importance assigned to health, few have systematically examined the health–burden relationship, largely because the two concepts have not always been clearly differentiated (e.g. George & Gwyther, 1986; Pratt et al., 1985). An exception is the study of Grad and Sainsbury (1963). They noted that if the relative's health was good, fewer problems were experienced in caring for the patient.

*Social resources*

Social support has been widely regarded as having a beneficial effect on well-being (Cohen & Wills, 1985). Considerable confidence has been expressed in the benefits to carers of having other people to help out or to talk to about their difficulties (Ball, 1986; Crossman et al., 1981; Jones & Vetter, 1984; Mace & Rabins, 1981; Norris, 1988; Storandt, 1983). Research data, however, have not always buttressed these widely espoused beliefs and have highlighted the many different forms that social support can take. To encompass these different meanings the more general label of social resources is used, referring to the quantity of the carer's social interaction, the amount of informal and formal assistance the carer receives, and the carer's awareness of the support available.

*Availability of social interaction*: In the present model, isolation from others is seen as a threat to carers' basic needs for belongingness. The importance of social interaction for carers has been widely documented in the caregiving literature. Isolation from friends and forsaking one's social life are among the problems most often mentioned by carers (Barnes et al., 1981; Cartwright et al., 1973; Chenoweth & Spencer, 1986; Equal Opportunities Commission, 1980; George & Gwyther, 1986; Grad & Sainsbury, 1963; Jones & Vetter, 1984; Sanford, 1975; Stephens & Christianson, 1986; Thompson & Haran, 1985). Furthermore, restrictions in social activity have been linked independently with carers' reports of distress and depression (Poulshock & Deimling, 1984).

*Informal assistance*: Family and friends are often in a position to help a primary carer through doing chores, lending a sympathetic ear, or visiting the carereceiver. Zarit et al. (1980) found that visits to the carereceiver by other family members were associated with greater carer well-being. They interpreted their results as an indication of the value of sharing responsibility for care through talking to other family members. Consistent with this interpretation is Pratt et al.'s (1985) finding that turning to the family for support was an effective coping strategy for caregivers of Alzheimer sufferers.

Other studies, however, have raised doubts about the effectiveness of informal assistance. Gilleard et al. (1984a) failed to find evidence of assistance being associated with lower carer burden. With four separate measures of informal support, Gilhooly (1984) also obtained non-significant results, except in relation to satisfaction with help given by relatives. Satisfaction was associated with carer well-being. Relying on a similar subjective evaluation of support, George and Gwyther (1986) found that those who felt they needed more support were more likely to be burdened.

This pattern of results suggests three interpretations. First, the direction of causality may differ from that implied in the Gilhooly (1984) and George and Gwyther (1986) studies. The significant results may be explained not by good informal support, but rather by a healthy outlook on life. Those who are happy about caregiving will be more likely to feel satisfied with their informal support, while those who are distressed will be discontented, regardless of the actual support provided.

Second, it may be that the informal social network is a mixed blessing to the overloaded caregiver. The carer may see acts of kindness from others as needing reciprocation of some kind (Ingersoll-Dayton & Antonucci, 1988), which may be an additional source of stress that undermines the benefits of the help provided.

Third, informal assistance may not be given to carers or accepted by them until the caregiving situation becomes stressful. Low support may therefore reflect little need rather than little care for the carer. If so, the relationship between support and burden becomes complex. On the one hand, support is likely to be forthcoming when the strain on carers is high and apparent. On the other hand, such support should alleviate burden. These effects would act against each other, accounting for the absence of significant findings in some studies.

In the current model, informal support is therefore regarded not only as a predictor of burden but as a factor mediating between burden and mental health. As such, informal support is similar to coping strategies. Both could be responses to rather than determinants of burden.

*Formal assistance*: Providing relief from caregiving demands is the main rationale for making formal services widely available to carers. Descriptions of the stresses and strains of home care invariably conclude with policy recommendations favouring respite care, day care, and home nursing services for the carereceiver, and support groups and welfare visits for the caregiver (Aronson & Lipkowitz,

1981; Barnes et al., 1981; Bergmann et al., 1978; Equal Opportunities Commission, 1980; Fengler & Goodrich, 1979; Jones & Vetter, 1984; Storandt, 1983; Zarit et al., 1986). Such services give caregivers freedom from the emotional pressure, ensure time to do other things, and share the responsibility of care, factors which Horowitz (1978) and Crossman et al. (1981) regard as central to understanding burden. Support groups also educate caregivers so that they have a better understanding of what is happening to them and a greater appreciation of the coping strategies available (Barnes et al., 1981; Brodaty & Griffin, 1983; Gwyther, 1988; Zarit & Zarit, 1982).

Users of support services are generally appreciative of the help received (Cartwright et al., 1973; Crossman et al., 1981; Kahan et al., 1985; Levin et al., 1983; Reifler & Eisdorfer, 1980; Sands & Suzuki, 1983). The data on the extent to which service use reduces burden, however, have not been consistent. Grad and Sainsbury (1963, 1968) demonstrated that formal support can reduce the degree of burden experienced by the carers of psychiatric patients. In another longitudinal study, Gilleard et al. (1984b) found that supporters of day hospital patients saw benefits to themselves in using the service, particularly over time.

Other studies which have been cross-sectional and compared users and non-users show either weak or no relationship between burden and the use of formal supports (Gilleard et al., 1984a; Pratt et al., 1985; Zarit et al., 1980). Gilhooly (1984) has explained some of this confusion through demonstrating that formal support incorporates a number of different programmes often with differing degrees of effectiveness. The other explanation is methodological. The longitudinal studies lack adequate control groups to provide bases for inferences about service effectiveness. The cross-sectional studies comparing users and non-users have not controlled for the selection factors influencing who becomes a user and who does not. Services are often only available to those whose need is greatest. Furthermore, lack of use through lack of knowledge of available services has repeatedly been identified as a widespread problem (Aronson & Lipkowitz, 1981; Equal Opportunities Commission, 1980; Robinson & Thurnher, 1979; Wheatley, 1979). Differences in both need and knowledge between user and non-user groups is likely to invalidate comparisons in terms of burden.

As with informal support, the amount of formal assistance is regarded as both a factor influencing burden and as a step taken in response to burden. The issue of knowledge of services available introduces a third possibility. Service use may not mediate the burden and mental health link so much as moderate it. In other words, burden may be strongly predictive of mental health in the non-user population but have very little predictive value in the user population. Formal assistance may buffer beneficiaries from the adverse effects which may follow from burden.

*Awareness of support*: Caregivers may report being well catered for in terms of acquaintances, friends, even confidants, and may be receiving assistance of various kinds. Nevertheless, they may not feel comfortable about sharing their caregiving responsibilities. The reasons vary. Doubts about others' capacity and willingness to cope, a sense of duty, guilt about deserting the carereceiver are a few. Awareness of family and friends who would be relied upon to share the caregiving load represents the third aspect of social resources included in Table 3.1.

Morycz (1985) has defined social support in a way which is very close to the notion of awareness. Carers were asked whether they were able to get someone to stay with the carereceiver and whether any other backup help existed. Both measures were negatively associated with burden. Awareness may prove to be the most important of the social resource predictors of burden. It could be argued that a social support system is not really supporting the caregiver unless it can be freely used. At the very least, reluctance to call for help or share the responsibility must place serious limitations on the effectiveness of supposedly available support.

As with the other assistance variables, awareness may be not only important to the development of burden, but also to whether or not burden leads to poor mental health. In this sense, a buffering effect is the most likely. Those who are aware of back-up are in a better position than those who are not in preventing burden from affecting general well-being.

*Material resources*

Caregiving responsibilities may be eased by suitable housing, equipment and medical supplies, as well as through access to professional services and paid help. Drawing on resources of this kind depends on the financial well-being of families. Money allows carers to employ someone to help in the house, to act as a companion to the carereceiver, to modify the home to accommodate the needs of all family members, and to organise time away from caring to recuperate.

The financial losses incurred through caring have been widely documented (Archbold, 1983; Equal Opportunities Commission, 1980; Grad & Sainsbury, 1963), but less attention has been directed to the effect of this loss on the quality of life of the caregiver. Fengler and Goodrich (1979) found that caregivers with poor morale had greater financial needs than those who did not. While acknowledging that low income reduced access to means that might make life more bearable, they point out that low income is also associated with other correlates of poor morale—social isolation and having to stay in the workforce. Thus, the extent to which access to material resources directly alleviates caregiving burden is unclear. Furthermore, these data do not rule out the possibility that material resources are not so much determinants of burden, as factors that moderate the burden and mental health relationship. Material resources, like personality, formal assistance and awareness, may define two types of carers—'the haves' and 'the have nots'. While 'the haves' are protected from poor mental health, 'the have nots' are vulnerable.

### Crises of decline

Awareness of degeneration, unpredictability, time constraints, the caregiver–carereceiver relationship, and choice restriction all have been postulated as serious threats to the basic needs of caregivers. To varying degrees these difficulties are likely to frustrate carers in their efforts to maintain a lifestyle which provides stability and security, love and belongingness, and regard for self.

#### Awareness of degeneration
Aronson and Lipkowitz (1981) refer to 'the slow extinction of the personality' (p. 568) in Alzheimer patients and Barnes et al. (1981) report caregivers 'grieving for the loss of their "dead" companion who (is) still physically present' (p. 82). These experiences are likely to be threatening to family carers in a number of ways. First, confronting death is likely to leave carers feeling insecure, making them consider their own mortality as well as that of their loved ones (Beckwith, 1988; Golden, 1982). Second, facing the lack of permanence in intimate relationships may threaten the carer's sense of belonging (Meier, 1988). Third, deterioration in the carereceiver's condition may leave some carers, particularly women caring for their husbands, feeling unsafe and afraid (Glick et al., 1974).

Degeneration, in its most extreme form, refers to the loss of skills which make human beings human. The emergence of behaviours which are destructive, dangerous or are widely regarded as a social embarrassment also fall into this category and have been given considerable attention in the caregiving literature, though the findings have not been interpreted within the present conceptual framework.

Studies have shown that caregiving strain is related to carereceivers being demanding, disruptive and disinterested in social interaction (Fengler & Goodrich, 1979; Greene et al., 1982; Morycz, 1985; Poulshock & Deimling, 1984). Carers themselves express concern about demanding, wandering and dangerous behaviours (Gilleard et al., 1984a; Grad & Sainsbury, 1963; Isaacs, 1971; Sanford, 1975; Wheatley, 1979), but appear to be remarkably tolerant of behavioural disturbances such as shouting, being rude to visitors, having temper tantrums, and using bad language (Gilleard et al., 1984a).

These findings suggest that the critical variable may not be anti-social behaviour per se, but rather persistent and irreversible anti-social behaviour. The types of behaviours which Gilleard et al. (1984a) found were well tolerated could be episodic with the prospect of positive social behaviour re-emerging. In contrast, the behaviours which have been found to pose more serious problems appear to be akin to those of Alzheimer patients whose 'sense of being' fades with time, never to re-emerge.

*Unpredictability*

Unpredictability in caregiving can be expected to threaten needs for security and stability, as well as needs for love and belongingness when accompanied by further deterioration in the carereceiver. The unpredictability hypothesis can be derived from a number of other sources. First, unpredictability has been a cornerstone of life event research. Any unexpected event is purported to have the potential for causing adjustment difficulties (Danish et al., 1980). Second, in their studies of caregiving, Fengler and Goodrich (1979) and Robinson and Thurnher (1979) found that lack of knowledge and the unexpectedness of the situation characterised carers who were having the greatest difficulty adjusting to the role. Third, professionals' accounts also suggest that being knowledgeable and prepared significantly increase the caregiver's capacity to care. Families are sometimes provided with little information about diseases, sometimes they have difficulty accepting the diagnosis, and sometimes they are unable to appreciate the progressive deterioration they will observe over time (Barnes et al., 1981; Chenoweth & Spencer, 1986). As a result, they may feel responsible and guilty about behavioural problems which are actually disease related, or they may have unrealistic expectations of the patient, resulting in feelings of hostility and antagonism. Either way, their unpreparedness is likely to increase their perceptions of threat.

*Time constraints*

A number of studies deal with carers' anguish at having to satisfy contradictory obligations at the same time (role conflict) and at having insufficient time to meet commitments (role overload). Cantor (1980) and Horowitz (1978) have recognised the loyalty and time problems facing caregivers with responsibilities across generations, that is, for their own family and a parent. Nissel's (1984) time diaries illustrate women's dual roles of home-maker and care provider, and Cantor (1980) and Horowitz (1978) provide insightful illustrations of women's commitment to these activities. Cantor found that women were prepared to make great personal sacrifices to ensure that neither generation suffered because of the competing demands of the other. Even more telling is Horowitz' observation that women protected their spouses from involvement in caregiving, even when the spouse's parent was the person receiving care.

The second area of role conflict and overload involves work and caregiving. Treas (1977) foreshadowed the competing responsibilities confronting women in the areas of marriage, offspring, parents, and work outside the home. Several years later, Brody and her co-workers (Brody, 1981; Brody et al., 1983) examined the attitudes of three generations of women and found that the potential for conflict had become a reality. The future caregivers adhered strongly to traditional values about family care, yet at the same time espoused egalitarian gender roles. Consistently, a minority of care-givers have reported giving up work because of their caregiving responsibilities (Brody & Schoonover, 1986; Cartwright et al., 1973; Equal Opportunities Commission, 1980; Jones & Vetter, 1984; Grad & Sainsbury, 1963; Wheatley, 1979). Others, however, have stayed in the workforce (Cantor, 1980), but not without personal costs. Promotions and advancement are often sacrificed (Equal Opportunities Commission, 1980). Archbold (1983) found that 'care managers', those who organised for others to provide essential services, were more likely to be in the workforce. Even so, care-managing activities were inclined to spill over into work time, and caregivers were not without feelings of overload and guilt when they came home to their frail elderly parent.

Studies which have related carer strain to having competing roles have produced inconsistent findings (Fengler & Goodrich, 1979; Gilhooly, 1984). Nevertheless, time constraints are expected to threaten basic needs on two fronts. When caregiving is in competition with other commitments and responsibilities, the chances of poor performance are likely to be increased and the carer's self-esteem decreased. Where the competing commitments involve friendships and family obligations, interpersonal relationships may become strained, and the fulfilment of belongingness and love needs may be jeopardised.

## The caregiver-carereceiver relationship

A destructive relationship between caregiver and carereceiver is likely to undermine the sense of worth of both of them, particularly when care is provided over long periods. At the same time, a close relationship is not necessarily non-threatening. The carer's belongingness and security may be threatened by the immi of a loved one. Spouse carers are particularly likely to be affected in this way. They are not just caring for family. They are trying to preserve their marital relationship.

Support for both these positions can be found in the literature. A number of studies have shown that strain is more likely to be found in relationships which were less than satisfactory in the first place (Fengler & Goodrich, 1979; Gilleard et al., 1984a; Horowitz & Shindelman, 1981). Cantor (1983), however, focused on the positive aspects of the relationship. She asked carers how strong their emotional attachment was to the carereceiver and obtained results which were directly opposite to those reported above. The greatest strain was experienced by carers who felt closest to their dependant. Two other studies which attempted to link the caregiver-carereceiver relationship to carer well-being have produced non-significant and weak positive effects (Gilhooly, 1984; Jenkins et al., 1985). In both these cases, a global positive or negative assessment of the quality of the relationship appears to have been made. If burden is a problem for the very close or the very distant carer, special nonlinear correlation coefficients will have to be used if an association between burden and the caregiver-carereceiver relationship is to be found.

## Choice restriction

While some carers assume their role with the belief that they have chosen the best option, others are resentful that they have no other options. Feelings of being trapped in the caring role are unlikely to promote the confidence and regard for oneself necessary to satisfying one's basic needs, leaving the unwilling provider of care vulnerable to burden.

The work which relates most closely to the issue of choice restriction has been reported by Cantor (1983). Cantor measured attitudes to providing care, but obtained results which were in the opposite direction to that predicted. Instead of finding poor adjustment among those with a negative attitude, Cantor found that most strain was experienced by carers who were committed to the view that families should accept their caregiving responsibilities.

One way of reconciling these findings is to consider the differences between commitment to family care and willingness to care. The high-commitment group is likely to comprise not only eager caregivers but also trapped caregivers. Trapped caregivers don't want to care, but duty and family obligation override all and provide them with no means of escape. They are likely to feel enormous strain in meeting their caring responsibilities. So too will eager carers, but in their case, close emotional ties are more likely to be the source of their difficulties.

## Conclusion

The research model is based on the stress paradigm with modifications made in the light of what we know about caring from previous research and observations. The model seeks parsimony by postulating direct links between three types of variables and burden. Workload encompasses the objective indices which current community policy assumes are linked to burden. The crises of decline are the less tangible aspects of care provision which are postulated as the greatest threats to carers. Resources are the crutches that carers may use so that caregiving does not pose as great a threat as it might otherwise. While all three are proposed as predictors of burden in their own right, resources are envisaged as having an additional mediating or moderating role to play in the burden-symptom relationship. Coping strategies, informal and formal support were regarded as possible mediators; self-esteem, mastery, emotionality, formal support, awareness of support, and financial well-being were possible moderators.

# 4 The sample of caregivers

A sample of 144 caregivers contributed to this study, 62 of whom were caring for a spouse, 73 for a parent or parent-in-law, and 9 for a relative or friend. Caregivers were approached through two community care programmes in the city of Canberra. One was a hospital outpatient programme, paid for totally out of public funds, providing day care for up to five days a week through one centre on the north side and another on the south side of the city. The other service was also totally publicly funded and provided regular home visits by nurses. Their assistance ranged from general information and advice to crisis counselling and nursing care.

Carers who agreed to participate in the study were contacted by one of three interviewers and meetings were arranged with them for a private discussion of their caregiving experiences. The interviews took place over two and sometimes three sessions, each about one-and-a-half hours long, and carers completed a questionnaire which was left with them after the first interview. Before looking more closely at the results, the sampling strategy and interviewing procedure should be discussed.

## Sampling caregivers

To care means to show concern for another's well-being and to ensure the provision of essential services. As such, we are all carers to some degree. The first task, therefore, was to derive a definition which clearly differentiated care which is out of the ordinary, from care which falls into the bounds of everyday life for most of us. Although the criteria would be unavoidably arbitrary, they needed to be precise and clear so as to define the population of interest. How much, how often and what type of assistance did the caregivers need to provide to be called caregivers? Should care managers (Archbold, 1983) be considered caregivers in view of the fact that they organise others to provide services rather than doing the work themselves? And must a caregiver assume responsibility for the well-being of the carereceiver to justify the tag of caregiver?

These considerations led to caregivers being defined as people who assume the major responsibility for providing or organising services on a regular basis to someone who is incapable of providing for her or himself. This definition incorporates the acceptance of responsibility for providing a service oneself or organising others to provide it. Major responsibility for service provision had to be in at least one of the following areas: The daily activities of (a) cleaning, (b) shopping or (c) meal preparation; self-care involving (d) washing, (e) dressing, (f) toileting or (g) mobility; or supervisory care involving (h) regular checks on well-being more than once in a day.

Finally, for practical purposes, paid providers of care (carers in receipt of a government welfare benefit do not fall into this category) and carers of children who were disabled or chronically ill were excluded from the population.

Having arrived at a set of rules defining a caregiver, a second hurdle had to be overcome—making contact. The major obstacle was the absence of a register of caregivers from which a sample could be selected. The option favoured, while less than perfect, was to contact carers through providers of community services. Other options entailed the screening of dwellings first (Rowland et. al., 1984), which would have been enormously expensive.

Of the agencies providing home care support, the Day Care Centres and the Community Nursing Service had the advantages of being widely known, widely available, and free of charge. Furthermore, caregivers could be readily contacted through them. In other more broadly based programmes, such as Meals on Wheels and Home Help, clients could have been without a caregiver and organised the service themselves. Furthermore, sampling through Meals on Wheels and Home Help would have led to an underrepresentation of carers who were young, able, female co-residents, since eligibility criteria assumed that when they were present, the frail aged were not in need of the service.

Thus, services were chosen to ensure as good a cross-section of caregivers as possible. This is not to say that the sampling procedure was without bias. Precluded from the sample were those who had not heard of the community programmes, who did not believe they had anything to offer, or who were unable to take advantage of the programmes because of the peculiarities of the caring situation (e.g. a dependant who refused to cooperate with anyone other than the caregiver). Another likely consequence of the sampling strategy was an overrepresentation of carers who had almost total responsibility for the well-being of the clients. The carers interviewed, therefore, were not only beneficiaries of community programmes, but they were beneficiaries of programmes geared to home care of the more dependent.

## Contacting caregivers

The caregivers of clients of the Day Care Centres and the Community Nursing Service were initially contacted by letter. To preserve client confidentiality, this letter was delivered by centre coordinators and community nurses. The names and addresses of those who were interested in participating were then forwarded to the research team so that an interview could be arranged. Responses were obtained from 69 carers of Day Centre clients (60 per cent of those contacted through the Day Centres) and 71 carers of Community Nursing clients (an estimated 32 per cent of those contacted through Community Nursing).[1] A further four people heard about the study, met our caring criteria, and volunteered to be interviewed. Of the 144 initial participants, six failed to complete the study by not taking part in the second interview. In five cases, caregivers were looking after two dependants rather than one. In these instances, the data from the more dependent person were used for the analyses.

## Interviewing caregivers

Interviews were conducted by myself and two other psychologists. All were experienced interviewers and all were women. To maximise compatibility, we used a highly structured questionnaire, developed from my unstructured interviews with past and present caregivers. Given the vast amount of information sought from carers, it was unrealistic to expect three different interviewers to collect data comprehensively and systematically without an explicit set of questions to guide them. At the same time, our experiences quickly told us that the subject matter lent itself far better to unstructured interviewing — caregiving is a complex topic, emotionally charged, and much of the information we required was not instantly accessible to the carers.

Differing reasons as to why people become caregivers complicated the matter. For instance, it was reasonable to ask a daughter or nephew why they were the ones to take on the caring role. But one could not ask the same question of a spouse. Similarly, a meaningful question for the caregiver of a physically able person concerned the chores with which the carereceiver assisted. For a paralysed recipient, however, the question did not arise.

In most cases, care was being provided to a loved one whose health was deteriorating, emotional circumstances that invariably evoked feelings of frustration and loss, to which people responded in very different ways. For some, control was of the utmost importance. Others desperately needed someone to talk to, and used the interview to release pent up feelings that were not shared with others close to the situation. Many a tear was shed during the interviews, and we as interviewers were often deeply moved by the stories carers had to tell. The diverse needs of the caregivers could not be adequately respected in a standardised interview.

The difficulty of accessibility arose from the inability of some carers to verbalise or even think about such sensitive topics as burden and institutionalisation. Structured interviewing would have committed the interviewer to questioning caregivers on such issues, thereby threatening both interview rapport and caregiver well-being.

Repression of highly emotional subject matter was not, however, the only source of accessibility problems. Caregivers often had relatively little time or energy to reflect on what they were doing and why. Asking caregivers about the functions they performed therefore raised issues on which they sometimes had no ready answers. Structured interviewing would have provided the caregiver with very limited opportunities for exploring their views about caregiving, and may have elicited only superficial responses.

The interview schedule was therefore designed to be as conversational as possible and interviewers were instructed to be flexible in its use. Factual non-threatening information was sought initially and sensitive issues were broached later after the caregiver and the interviewer had got to know each other a little better. The general strategy was to ease caregivers gently into discussion of more sensitive issues and to intersperse straightforward non-threatening questions throughout the interviews as tension breakers. Interviewers were given certain liberties. Emphasis was placed on capturing the atmosphere of an informal interview by listening to whatever the caregiver wanted to say, by making changes to the order of questions to maintain the flow and build rapport, by probing gently when respondents had difficulty answering, and by leaving sensitive issues until the caregiver was ready to face them. By adopting this approach, we hoped to give caregivers the opportunity to convey their caregiving experiences to us in some depth: For some this was an opportunity that they had never had before.

Where carers consented, interviews were tape recorded to ensure information was not lost in the less structured sessions, and to check comparability across interviewers. Interviews were conducted either in the homes of caregivers or at The Australian National University, according to the caregiver's preference. While the university setting ensured greater privacy for the carer, home interviews avoided transport difficulties and problems of leaving carereceivers alone for too long. From our perspective, home interviews offered the opportunity of catching a glimpse of caring in action, and, on occasions, of meeting and chatting with those receiving care. At times, care-receivers became interested in the purpose of our visit and joined in. Under such circumstances, factual information was collected initially, and arrangements were made to talk to the caregiver alone on the following occasion. Where interruptions were unavoidable, and attitudes and opinions were being sought, caregivers were asked to read the questions from the interview schedule and respond in writing.

In summary, the interviewing approach can best be described as one which tried to achieve as much structure as possible, without either jeopardising rapport, or depriving caregivers of the opportunity to make sense of their experiences and communicate their views. In practice, this meant that conversational interviewing was interspersed to varying degrees with highly structured questioning.

# 5   Who cares?

The representativeness of the sample of caregivers was gauged by comparing results with those reported in other studies. We also explored the emergence of the caregiving relationship and analysed the importance of such factors as gender, geographical proximity, and personal suitability in taking on the caregiver role. Finally, carers' future expectations were examined, along with a limited amount of data on what the future actually held for them two-and-a-half years later.

## Socio-demographic characteristics

The majority of those interviewed were caring for a parent or parent-in-law (51 per cent), a sizeable minority cared for a spouse (43 per cent), and a very small minority cared for a relative or friend (6 per cent). The carers' ages covered a wide range from 26 to 82 years with a mean of 58 years ($SD = 13.04$). The majority (51 per cent) were 60 years of age or older. As might be expected, spouse carers were substantially older than the other carers. While 93 per cent of spouse carers were elderly themselves, only 19 per cent of those caring for someone other than a spouse fell into this category.[1]

Three-quarters of the caregivers were women. The percentage was even higher among those caring for someone other than a spouse (87 per cent). The gender bias virtually disappeared, however, when caregiving within marriage was examined. Forty per cent of spouse carers were men, 60 per cent women. This difference is inconsequential given that women have greater longevity and tend to marry men who are older than themselves. While the percentage of men in the Australian population was 51 per cent at 50 years of age (the average age of non-spouse carers), the figure drops to 46 per cent among those who were 69 years of age (the mean age of non-spouse carers), and 42 per cent among 75 year olds (Australian Bureau of Statistics, 1986).

A significant percentage of caregivers were engaged in paid work (29 per cent), a pattern which was particularly strong among those caring for someone other than a spouse (43 per cent). Over a quarter of non-spouse carers also had children under sixteen years (28 per cent), and almost three-quarters were married or in de facto relationships (72 per cent).

A final statistic which was useful for comparisons with other studies was the living arrangement of caregiver and carereceiver. The overwhelming majority (86 per cent) of caregivers lived with their dependants, regardless of whether or not the person receiving care was a spouse. Of those not caring for a spouse, 70 per cent had the carereceiver living with them, 7 per cent resided in the care-receiver's house, 12 per cent occupied separate dwellings, and 11 per cent of carereceivers had self-contained flats attached to the caregiver's house.

These statistics were compared with those from five other sources, two based on large community samples in the United States (Special Committee on Aging, United States Senate, 1987; Stephens & Christianson, 1986), one on a smaller community sample in Australia (Australian Council on the Ageing and the Australian Department of Community Services, 1985), and two from Britain where carers were traced through placement offers in a psychogeriatric day hospital (Gilleard et al., 1984a) and two general medical practices (Jones & Vetter, 1984).

Overall, socio-demographic characteristics were similar across studies, with two exceptions. This sample underrepresented carers who lived apart from their dependant as well as those who were looking after someone other than a spouse, parent or parent-in-law.

A further bias in the present study was an overrepresentation of higher status occupational groups: 38 per cent of families had a breadwinner in a professional or managerial occupation, 46 per cent in a skilled, clerical or administrative occupation, and 17 per cent in an unskilled or semi-skilled occupation. The overrepresentation of the more privileged has been recognised as a major problem of research into caregiving (George & Gwyther, 1986). In order to contain sampling costs, caregivers are usually contacted through services and organisations, and there is some evidence that service use is class biased. Drawing on data from the United States and Britain, Le Grand (1982) has argued that the middle classes received more health care relative to need than the working classes, even in circumstances where the services were free. In addition to this bias, the population of Canberra has a higher proportion of white-collar workers than other capital cities in Australia (Young, 1985). This compounds the problem of underrepresentation of the poor.

*Characteristics of carereceivers*

Those being cared for ranged in age from 23 to 100 years, the average being 77 years ($SD = 10.53$). All but five were 60 years of age or more. Since caregiving for the younger carereceivers did not differ substantially from that for older carereceivers, they were included in all analyses. The majority of carereceivers were women (61 per cent), although the reverse was true in spouse-caring situations. Where spouses were providing care, the receiver was more likely to be male (60 per cent). Those being cared for by a spouse also tended to be younger, their mean age being 73 years ($SD = 8.79$) compared with 80 years ($SD = 10.66$) for non-spouse recipients.

### Carereceivers' health

Cardio-vascular disorders afflicted 48 per cent of carereceivers, injury, arthritis, or some other muscular-skeletal disorder was a problem for 36 per cent, impaired mobility as a result of stroke affected 28 per cent, dementia, senility, memory loss, or disorientation was mentioned in 27 per cent of cases, and gastro-intestinal disorders afflicted 19 per cent. The pattern was the same for spouse and non-spouse carers in all cases but stroke. A larger proportion of those who were being cared for by a spouse had suffered a stroke (39 per cent compared with 21 per cent in non-spouse caring situations).

### Relocation of carereceivers

The majority of carereceivers had moved house in the last five years (53 per cent) or since needing care (56 per cent). Relocation was significantly less likely, however, where care was being provided to a spouse. Only 32 per cent of couples had moved house in the last five years and only 40 per cent since care was required by one partner. Reasons for moving from other regions, as most did, were associated with seeking family support. Couples wanted to be near their children (19 per cent), while others moved because they were unable to care for themselves (45 per cent).

### Circumstances of caring

The sample was almost evenly divided on whether the caring role was acquired suddenly (52 per cent) or gradually (48 per cent). When questioned about the reasons for caring, spouses attributed their carer role to a specific health problem (79 per cent), most commonly stroke, surgery or injury. Non-spouse caregivers were less likely to care because of a specific illness, and more likely to assume the role through general deterioration, loneliness or widowhood (61 per cent).

The most likely explanation for these differences is age. Those being cared for by their families rather than a spouse are the survivors. With increasing age, general deterioration and loneliness (particularly through widowhood) are more likely to pose threats to independent living.

An alternative explanation which cannot be ruled out is that the contribution of spouse carers in cases of general deterioration is underrepresented. Spouses supporting partners who are gradually deteriorating may not identify with the caregiving role. The care provided is a continuation of that given during a lifetime and gradual changes may go unnoticed.

## Who accepts the role?

Shanas (1979a, 1979b) has put forward the notion of a care hierarchy operating in western society. If a spouse is available and able, the spouse will be the caregiver. If there is no spouse, children will assume the role. Where neither spouse nor child can provide care, siblings, nieces and nephews are more likely to provide the necessary support.

**Figure 5.1  The frequency of types of caring dyads and of closer kin**

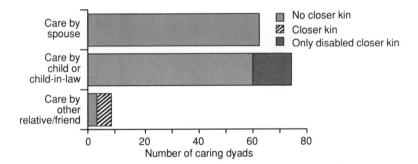

The pattern of care observed in this research was consistent with Shanas' (1979a, 1979b) observations (see Figure 5.1). Of the 75 caregiving situations where a spouse was alive, 62 were the providers of care. In the 13 remaining cases, spouses were either hospitalised, institutionalised, or in need of care themselves, and children had assumed responsibility.

In the 82 non-spouse-caring situations, 73 of the caregivers were children or children-in-law. Of the other nine, four had no living children and were cared for by grandchildren, a niece, and a nephew. The remaining five were exceptions to the caring hierarchy: Immediate family had relinquished their responsibilities, leaving care provision to companions, a niece-in-law, a sister-in-law, and an ex-wife.

If a spouse was well and able there was little ambiguity in who would provide care—in choosing a marriage partner, one chose a caregiver. There was greater latitude, however, in whom the next of kin would be to accept the responsibility for care when no spouse was available. Caregivers generally had brothers and sisters who were as closely related to the dependant, and, therefore, just as eligible for the responsibility (see Figure 5.2).

Research has consistently shown caregiving to be women's work. Gender is the major predictor of who will care when a partner is either not present or not able to provide support (Jones & Vetter, 1984; Special Committee on Aging, United States Senate, 1987; Stephens & Christianson, 1986). This same pattern emerged in the present study. The overwhelming majority of carers were daughters or daughters-in-law of the carereceiver. The extent to which there were others in the family who could have become the caregiver is the first step in understanding how these women came to assume the role.

**Figure 5.2   The frequency of types of non-spouse carers and other eligible carers**

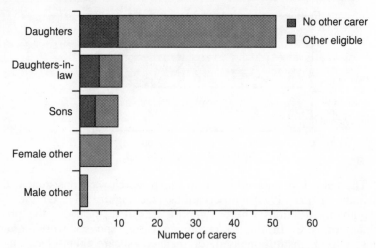

The largest group of carers after spouses comprised 51 daughters caring for a parent (62 per cent of the non-spouse carers). From Figure 5.2 it can be seen that only a fifth of this group had no living sibling. In fact, just over half of these women had at least one brother (55 per cent) and just under half had at least one sister (45 per cent).

The next largest group was daughters-in-law (13 per cent). In all cases, their husbands were alive and well. Paid workforce participation by men and not women explained the caring arrangement in six of the 11 families. Daughters-in-law were at home with the elderly parent while sons were employed outside the home. In the remaining five families, women were not so readily available to meet the needs of their parent-in-law. They too were in the workforce, in four cases full-time. One can only assume that these women accepted care for their husband's parent as an extension of their traditional nurturing role within the family.

Caregiving by daughters-in-law was not primarily because there were no other brothers or sisters in the family. Of the 11 cases, two carereceivers had another son, two had a daughter, and two had other sons as well as daughters. Where a daughter was available, differences in employment status did not explain care by daughters-in-law rather than daughters.

The third group, almost the same size as the second, were sons caring for parents (12 per cent). In five of the ten cases, no daughter was available to fill the role. Indeed four had no siblings. Given the previously noted tendency of daughters-in-law to assume the caring role, it was of interest that six of the ten sons were unmarried.

Among the last ten cases, care was provided by women in all but two. The men who provided care were retired while their wives worked. One cared for his mother-in-law, while the other cared for his aunt. For all ten caregivers, there were others as closely or more closely related to the dependant who could have provided care.

These results indicate that in 77 per cent of non-spouse caring situations, there were men or women, as closely related to the dependant as the caregiver, who could have taken on the role. Women unquestionably did more than their share of caregiving. Furthermore, the considerably lower contribution of men could not be explained entirely by paid workforce participation. The involvement of daughters-in-law in care even though they had full-time jobs illustrated the strength of the traditional nurturing role in women's lives. Lieberman (1978) reported that when it came to care of ageing parents, women rather than men were the 'kin-keepers' — they were more likely to see change in their parents and be preoccupied and bothered by it.

This is not to suggest, however, that women have a special aptitude for the caring role. As Cantor (1980), Soldo and Myllyluoma (1983), and Noelker and Wallace (1985) have found, the marital bond makes the strongest claim on caregiving obligation. Indeed, for many men in this study, the nurturant role was accepted without resentment or doubt: 'It's no big deal. She looked after me for 17 years — I've only been doing this for eight'; 'My wife worked really hard. She did so much for me and the family. She had a hard life. It's my turn now — to look after her.'

In the vast majority of cases there was no evidence of what Ungerson (1987) has called negotiation between husbands and daughters as to who should care. In one case there was clearly tension between a husband and his step-daughter, with the former upset by the daughter 'not caring enough about her mother'. This may have been an instance of a male carer trying to off-load chores onto a female relative, but this kind of behaviour was the exception, not the rule. In this study, men cared for their wives willingly, expressing the view that it was their responsibility, not their children's. 'They have their own lives to lead' was the most frequently heard response from both husbands and wives.

Furthermore, while men were not well represented among the ranks of non-spouse carers, it should not be overlooked that a small proportion (8 per cent out of the 13 per cent male non-spouse carers) had accepted the responsibility even though they had sisters eligible for the role. While gender is important, there are clearly other factors entering into the decision of who will care.

When asked, 'Who else was there who could have become [the] carer...?', most were prepared to give at least one alternative (75 per cent) and 35 per cent more than two. When asked the question, 'Why have you become the carer rather than...[them]?', the answers varied considerably. Beliefs about being able to offer a superior quality of life in terms of geographical location, living arrangements, or family atmosphere were most frequently expressed by carers (31 per cent). One carer thought her grandmother would like to be absorbed into 'a big happy family where there was lots going on'. Another thought that the dry climate would better suit her father's respiratory problems.

In contrast to these positive views were less committed responses—other potential carers refusing (28 per cent) and having no alternative (25 per cent). With two exceptions, those in the latter category were caring for parents who had no other living children. Where others refused to care, the alternative providers tended to be the carer's siblings, although one third saw their sisters and brothers-in-law as the major obstacles.

The next three most popular reasons related to the quality of the caregiver–carereceiver relationship. In just over a fifth of families (22 per cent), the carereceiver chose the caregiver. One such response was, 'I think she knew that my sister would be tougher to live with than me. She knows she can get around me'. Almost as sizeable a group (20 per cent) were those who said they had a good relationship with the dependant (e.g., 'We have always been close—she will talk to me'), but sometimes it was a case of the carer having the best relationship within a not-so-harmonious set of relationships ('The others can't stomach her nor her them—but I have an affinity for old ladies'). Much the same percentage (19 per cent) replied to the question, 'Why you?' with the simple response, 'That's what I wanted'. According to one carer, 'I always was the one who watched out for her'.

The next most popular response was that others were unable to care because of their commitments (18 per cent). Alternative carers were seen to be too busy, most often because of young families and work, and occasionally because they were already caring for an elderly relative. Having the alternative carers living at too great a distance from the carereceiver, sometimes overseas, ranked eighth (13 per cent).

Of the remaining responses only one was of interest, not because of its frequency, but because of the prejudice it highlights. For four of the caregivers, their unmarried status was seen to be the major determinant of their becoming the carer. With no family responsibilities of their own, they were seen by family members to be the ideal providers of care. As one caregiver put it: 'All the family expected this of me.' Such a resolution to the 'who cares' issue is certainly egalitarian, in that it ensures that every family member is experiencing the caregiving role be it in relation to a child, a spouse, or a parent. The only element of unfairness is the issue of choice. The unmarried child seems to have none.

Furthermore, to the extent that the unmarried have eschewed family responsibility, their suitability to the caring role can be questioned. In terms of personality and experience, they may well be the ones least equipped to cope with a frail elderly parent. To assume that everyone can and should nurture dependants is to deny the rights of those who neither seek nor find fulfilment in family life. To thrust family obligations upon such persons may not be in the interest of either caregiver or carereceiver.

It should be added, however, that expecting unmarried children to provide assistance to frail parents is not a universal phenomenon, particularly when the child is male. For one young man, being unmarried meant instant disregard by his sister. 'He couldn't possibly look after Mum', she said, 'he hasn't got a wife yet'.

*Geographical proximity*

One factor which could have been expected to feature more prominently in answers to the 'why you' question was the geographical proximity of caregiver and carereceiver. Only a relatively small percentage (13 per cent) attributed others' non-involvement to being too far away. Nevertheless, distance may underlie more popular reasons given by respondents. A history of living close to dependants may foster greater intimacy and lead caregivers to believe that their environment is optimal. In contrast, distance may facilitate refusal to be involved.

The first issue examined was the extreme case of proximity: How frequently do caregiver and carereceiver share a residence prior to the dependency of the latter? This occurred in only 17 per cent of cases. For the vast majority of caregivers, providing support was not a consequence of cohabitation. A change in living patterns was the norm.

The next issue was whether or not caregivers were less inclined to become involved if they were at some distance from the dependant. Rowland (1986) reported that 87 per cent of the aged in Sydney had at least one child also living in the city. If proximity is a determinant of who cares, non-spouse-caring partnerships involving moves to other cities should be in the minority.

The data from this study do not support such a prediction. As mentioned earlier, 67 per cent of relatives needing care from someone other than a spouse had moved interstate, in most cases coming from New South Wales (36 per cent) and Victoria (17 per cent). Most non-spouse caregivers brought their dependants (57 per cent) to them; only 10 per cent of caregivers and dependants had moved to Canberra together. Among those carereceivers who moved, 35 per cent had no children in their home town, but did have children in Canberra. The remaining 32 per cent had children both at home and in Canberra. Thus, approximately a third had to move to Canberra to be cared for by a child, another third moved to Canberra for care in spite of eligible caregivers at home, and the final third had their caregivers at home in Canberra.

The high mobility observed in this sample of dependants may not be typical of other regions. Canberra has a significantly younger and more mobile population than other Australian cities (Rowland, 1979; Young, 1985), and has a high proportion of young families who do not have relatives here (Young, 1985). In two separate studies (Lewis, 1975; Saha, 1975), the proportion with no relatives in Canberra was estimated to be approximately 50 per cent. In other words, Canberra has attracted 'the birds who have flown the coop'.

Nevertheless, the conclusion can be drawn from these data that distance from a parent does not imply abandonment. The majority of those who provided care to someone other than a spouse in Canberra are responding to the needs of a geographically distant parent.

A third avenue for exploring why some assume the caring role while others do not is to look behind carers' perceptions of their 'superior environment'. In part, these perceptions relate to physical characteristics, such as climate, housing, cost of living, and access to hospitals. While these kinds of issues were mentioned by various carers, none emerged with notable consistency. The other aspect of offering a 'superior environment' has to do with things like tolerance of disability, knowledge about caring for the elderly, and competence. Although carers did not explain their caregiving in these terms, such variables were measured independently, providing an opportunity to assess the extent to which these qualities typified the caregiving population.

*Knowledge and competence*

Only a small minority of non-spouse caregivers (14 per cent) reported feelings of lack of competence initially and almost half (49 per cent) described themselves as feeling very competent. Just over half (53 per cent), however, admitted that there were some or quite a lot of things they had to learn about caregiving. In the words of one carer, 'I had to learn to sensitively take control of another person's life, yet not live it for him — let him participate and respect him'. For a second, 'It's very different from what you imagine. There's no such word as HURRY'. In the case of one young man, caregiving meant, 'Learning to nurture a parent rather than rebel'. Developing a caring personality in the sense of having patience, showing sensitivity, and preserving the self-respect of the care recipient was mentioned by 48 per cent of non-spouse caregivers, while treating and managing the illness (e.g. giving injections and handling falls) was new to 32 per cent.

Thus, not all non-spouse caregivers were fully equipped to provide care initially, even though the majority felt confident. Caregiving is not a role that falls only on the shoulders of those who are knowledgeable.

*Tolerance*

Yet another possible psychological determinant of who cares is tolerance of disability. To assess how accepting non-spouse caregivers were of the physical and mental failings of their carereceivers and how resilient they were in dealing with these changes, we asked them to nominate the circumstances that would lead them to seek alternative care and whether or not they were aware of having a breaking point. Over half (56 per cent) could specify the sorts of disabilities which would lead them to discontinue care. Included were the familiar obstacles to home care such as incontinence and immobility as well as not so common difficulties such as 'cleaning mum's false teeth'. Approximately three-quarters of caregivers (76 per cent) were only too aware of having a breaking point. For these caregivers, tolerance for frailty in the elderly was not infinite; there were real limits.

To draw inferences from this is difficult because of the absence of a comparison group. While carers are not perfect in terms of competence, knowledge and tolerance, they may have more of these qualities than their relatives. It is interesting to note, however, that these carers scored no better than the group who had least choice in who would assume the caring role—spouse carers.

## Expectations of the future

Care had been provided on average for 5.52 years ($SD$ = 6.66). Six per cent had been caring for less than six months, 63 per cent for fewer than five years; and 14 per cent for more than ten years. The longest commitment had been made by a daughter who had cared for her 100-year-old mother for 45 years. Care had been provided in spite of a broken marriage and major health problems for herself and her children—circumstances which would have led most to seek alternative caring arrangements. Only months after our interview, her mother died.

When carers were asked how long they intended to provide care, were they aware of a breaking point, and would they consider accepting an offer of a place in a nursing home, the answers from spouse and non-spouse carers differed notably. They confirmed Gilleard's (1984b) finding that spouses show greater commitment to the caring role.

An overwhelming percentage of spouse caregivers (87 per cent) intended to care 'as long as ... [the dependant] is alive' or 'as long as I am able'. Thirty-nine per cent admitted to having a breaking point in relation to the future provision of care. For 12 per cent, the breaking point was internal—simply not realising their own limits. For a further 8 per cent, the crucial factor was having the dependant bedridden, and for 7 per cent the breaking point was incontinence.

In contrast, non-spouse caregivers were somewhat less committed to providing care in the future. Less than half (44 per cent) said they would care indefinitely (i.e., until the dependant died or they could no longer provide care), and the majority (76 per cent) were aware of a breaking point. Most frequently mentioned breaking points were carers not realising their own limits (24 per cent) or care-receivers becoming frail (19 per cent), incontinent (14 per cent), or bedridden (10 per cent).

Only caregivers who had lodged an application at a nursing home or hostel were presented with the scenario of receiving an offer. Overall, neither spouse nor non-spouse carers were prepared to accept an offer at the time of the interview. Those caring for someone other than a spouse, however, were significantly more willing to take up an offer. Out of the 53 per cent of non-spouse carers on waiting lists, 23 per cent would have accepted an offer. Almost as many spouse carers were on waiting lists (41 per cent), but only 7 per cent were ready to accept at the time of the interview. Indeed, some saw the option as only a backstop should something happen to them. A wife replied that she'd 'continue until [she was] dead or invalided'. For a husband, the hope was that he would not need it — that he and his wife would 'die on the same day at home'.

## Realities of the future

And what *did* the future hold for the 62 spouse and 82 non-spouse caregivers? At the time of writing, two-and-a-half years after the first interview and one year after the last, the lives of the majority had changed dramatically.

The follow-up data for the day care sample was almost complete, unlike the community nursing sample. The day care sample, therefore, provided the best basis for comparing spouse and non-spouse caregivers. Their futures did not differ significantly (see Table 5.1). In each group, the minority continued to provide care, 38 per cent overall. The majority were no longer caregivers, primarily because their dependants had entered an institution (38 per cent) or had died (20 per cent). In one case the caregiver had died before the carereceiver, and in another case, an alternative carer had taken over.

As of September 1985, the tally for all caregivers stood as follows. The future of 24 was not known. Sixty-four caregivers were no longer providing care. Thirty dependants were receiving care in institutions, three dependants had changed caregivers, 29 dependants had died, and two caregivers had died. Of the original 144, only 56 caring dyads were still intact.

**Table 5.1  The percentage of spouse and non-spouse carers who had continued and discontinued caring one year after the completion of fieldwork**

| Caring status | Caregiver | |
|---|---|---|
| | Spouse (n=27) % | Non-spouse (n=42) % |
| Caring continues | 41 | 35 |
| Dependant died | 33 | 12 |
| Dependant institutionalised | 22 | 48 |
| Carer died | 4 | 0 |
| Don't know | 0 | 5 |

**Summary**

A diversity of factors lead individuals to assume care for another. For the vast majority of spouses, choice of a carer is not an issue. When children and other relatives become involved in caring, however, a number of people can be seen as potential carers. In practice, women are far more likely to assume responsibility than their male counterparts. Non-spouse carers can be roughly divided into three groups in answer to the question, 'who cares?' or more typically, 'which woman will care?'. Some care because there is no-one else (25 per cent), a somewhat larger proportion care because others will not or cannot become involved (34 per cent), and an even larger number care because they believe they will do it best (41 per cent).

# 6    Are caregivers burdened?

As we have seen, burden refers to caregivers' perceptions of the
extent to which caring interferes with their basic needs. The consequences of this definition should be discussed, however, because
carers' perceptions of deprivation may not correspond to others',
and their views of the cause of deprivation may not be shared by
outsiders. This definition excludes caring circumstances which,
intuitively, some would like to include. For instance, a caregiver
with serious health problems who refuses to acknowledge that
caregiving is threatening her well-being would not meet the criteria.
In this situation, observers could be expected to have a very
different perspective on the extent to which caregiving demands are
interfering with basic needs, and therefore, on whether or not the
situation is burdensome. In contrast, caring situations which outsiders consider unworthy of consideration as instances of burden
may be included. A caregiver who maintains that she has been
driven to the verge of a breakdown will be regarded as a person
experiencing burden, even if observers believe that her caregiving
responsibilities are not particularly onerous.

The defence of the present definition of burden lies in Thomas'
(1951) thesis that if actors 'define situations as real they are real in
their consequences' (p. 81). In the caregiving context, beliefs and
feelings about deprivation are postulated as being an integral part of
well-being and of central importance in determining how caregivers
will respond to providing care in the future. Nevertheless, some will
maintain that burden, as currently conceived, is only of limited use
for social policy. This is not the case.

The alternative to having an abstract subjective concept of burden
is one which ties burden to specific, observable and measurable
characteristics — an approach which has much immediate appeal. To
do this ad hoc may lead to a relatively uncontaminated catch, but
whether there is anything in the net of significance for policy
formulation is another matter. To assume, for instance, that burden
is the daily activities and personal care tasks provided for another is
to oversimplify caregiving to the point of meaninglessness. Caregiving is a relationship between two people, and it has all the

complexities of intimate human relationships. Any discussion of burden must take this into account, just as any judgement of child custody requires an understanding of the pressures on a family from all quarters. To infer burden on the basis of how many tasks are being performed for a dependant is as tunnel-visioned as assigning custody on the basis of who has most contact with the child.

The role which social scientists can play in these circumstances is to analyse the complexities of the caring relationship and develop a model for understanding and predicting burden. First, burden must be defined and measured for research purposes so that it is meaningful. The definition must incorporate the essential features; sidestepping them in the name of tightness and precision reduces the relevance of the enterprise. Having arrived at a meaningful definition, the researcher is in a position to focus on specific, observable and measurable characteristics as independent variables. If these emerge as significant correlates of burden, they can then be used as indicators of high-risk burden situations. Thus, the ultimate research criterion should remain as the caregiver's assessment of how she or he is managing. The policy-maker's criteria can be the specific characteristics of the caregiving situation which predispose the individual to such an appraisal.

Such a strategy, of course, holds for most people, but not all. This is indeed a problem when decisions about assistance have to be made for individuals. There will be people who are exceptions to the rule, and who risk not receiving much needed support. The problem is not peculiar to the caregiving situation, however. The compensation is that overall, the experiences of individuals are taken into account by this approach.

**Measuring burden**

The measurement of burden presented a number of difficulties. Caregivers could not be asked directly to indicate the extent to which their basic needs—physiological, safety, love or self-esteem needs—were threatened by caregiving demands. Such questioning would be jargon-ridden, arousing either suspicion or confusion in caregivers. The solution was to translate these abstract psychological concepts into real problems faced by caregivers.

Physiological needs require little elaboration; safety needs refer to a basic desire for shelter, protection from danger, order, and stability. Caregiving is known to threaten carers' physiological and safety needs. At the most fundamental level are threats to sleep, rest and health. Threats to order, stability and security can result when caregiving interferes with work, both paid and unpaid, makes planning difficult, and destroys household routine. Questions to the caregiver about inadequate rest, poor health, disrupted routine, task incompletion, and constant interruption were a straightforward matter. Not so questions about threats to the need for love and belongingness. This proved to be a particularly sensitive issue among caregivers because many avoided thinking about it. The issue was broached indirectly through questions assessing carers' feelings of divided loyalties between the carereceiver and other family members, and through carers' feelings of resentment at what had happened to the carereceiver. Threats to self-esteem were approached a little more easily through perceptions of inadequate performance and feelings of guilt, lack of control, and ignorance.

The relevant questions were, part of a longer list of caregiving experiences which caregivers rated in the self-completion questionnaire. They were asked to indicate if caregiving had led to these experiences, and if so, how much of a problem each was for them. For the purposes of measuring burden, however, difficulty ratings were disregarded. The items were scored with 1 meaning no, the caregiver had not had the experience, and 2 meaning yes, the caregiver had.

From the results of a factor analysis of the items, two scales were developed, one called Disruption, the other Inadequacy (see Table 6.1). The disruption scale comprised eight items and was concerned

**Table 6.1  The disruption and inadequacy scales and the percentage of caregivers endorsing each item (N=138)**

| Scales and items | % |
| --- | --- |
| Disruption | |
| Having to constantly be on call to assist the person you are caring for | 90 |
| Being unable to get your household chores done | 79 |
| Having to change your plans at the last minute | 71 |
| Being unable to get enough sleep | 64 |
| Being unable to rest when ill yourself | 64 |
| Having health problems as a result of caregiving | 44 |
| Not being able to do your job as well as you'd like | 42 |
| Inadequacy | |
| Feeling that you cannot get on top of all the things you have to do | 88 |
| Losing patience with the person you are caring for | 87 |
| Feeling that you are not doing anything as well as you should | 69 |
| Feeling guilty about what you have or have not done for the person you are caring for | 68 |
| Feelings of resentment at what has happened to the person you are caring for | 63 |
| Feeling divided loyalties between the person you are caring for and other members of your family | 62 |
| Feeling you have lost control over your life | 62 |
| Feeling that you don't understand the nature of the other person's illness | 59 |
| Feelings of resentment that this has happened to you | 59 |

with deprivation of physiological and safety needs. Scores ranged from 8 to 16 with a mean of 13.20 ($SD$ = 2.28). The distribution of scores was skewed with almost three-quarters of caregivers (74 per cent) experiencing at least four of the eight indices of basic need frustration. In other words, the majority had had their lives severely disrupted through being a primary care provider. The most widely endorsed items were having to constantly be on call (90 per cent), being unable to get the household chores done (79 per cent), and having to change plans at the last minute (71 per cent) (see Table 6.1). The alpha reliability coefficient for the disruption scale was .78.

The inadequacy scale had nine items and tapped feelings of frustration and dissatisfaction associated with personal loss and caregiving performance. Scores ranged from 9 to 18 with a mean of 15.20 ($SD$ = 2.54). Again the distribution was skewed, the majority being familiar with feelings of inadequacy and loss in the caregiving situation. Five or more items were endorsed by 74 per cent of caregivers. The most common experiences were not being able to get on top of things (88 per cent) and losing patience with the person being cared for (87 per cent). The alpha reliability coefficient for this scale was .80. Not surprisingly, those with high scores on the inadequacy scale also had high scores on the disruption scale, the Pearson correlation coefficient being .45 ($N$ = 135, $p$<.001).

The experience of burden was expected to correlate significantly with poor mental health. To test this prediction, caregivers were assessed on two measures of minor psychiatric symptoms — Bedford, Foulds and Sheffield's (1976) scales of anxiety and depression from the Delusions-Symptoms-States Inventory (DSSI/sAD) and Henderson, Byrne and Duncan-Jones' (1981) Four Neurotic Symptoms (4-NS). As anticipated, the higher the reports of disruption and inadequacy, the greater the likelihood of minor psychiatric symptoms (see Table 6.2).

The burden scales were also found to correlate significantly with Bradburn's (1969) Affect Balance Scale (see Table 6.2). Of considerable interest was the way in which the scales correlated differently with positive and negative affect. According to Bradburn, negative affect and positive affect are independent of each other. Negative affect is most likely to be influenced by life's problems and difficulties. In contrast, positive affect has more to do with the individual's involvement with other people, activities and interests.

For the caregiving group as a whole, the burden scales correlated with negative affect, but not positive affect. The absence of any relationship with positive affect was somewhat unexpected since caregiving is known to restrict caregivers' involvement in the world outside. This is particularly so for spouse caregivers who tend to live

**Table 6.2  The correlations of the disruption and inadequacy scales with selected validating scales for spouse, non-spouse, and all caregivers**

| General stress measure | Spouse caregivers n=53[a] | | Non-spouse caregivers n=74[b] | | All caregivers N=127[c] | |
|---|---|---|---|---|---|---|
| | Disruption | Inadequacy | Disruption | Inadequacy | Disruption | Inadequacy |
| DSSI/sAD | .36** | .28* | .38*** | .29** | .37*** | .26*** |
| 4-NS | .20 | .39*** | .41*** | .38*** | .32*** | .38*** |
| Affect balance | -.30* | -.39*** | -.08 | -.11 | -.17* | -.20* |
| Positive affect | -.24* | -.22* | .14 | .17 | .00 | .07 |
| Negative affect | .31** | .42*** | .27** | .36*** | .27*** | .40*** |

*Notes:* a  This is the minimum sample size for any single correlation. The maximum is 57
  b  This is the minimum sample size for any single correlation. The maximum is 79
  c  This is the minimum sample size for any single correlation. The maximum is 135

  *  $p < .05$    **  $p < .01$    ***  $p < .001$

alone with their dependants, to be isolated from external stimulation, and for whom the sources of positive affect are especially limited. Non-spouse caregivers, on the other hand, could have other family members at home to act as a distraction from caregiving stresses and to provide an alternative source of positive affect.

This interpretation was supported by analyses of the relationship between positive affect and burden for spouse and non-spouse caregivers separately (see Table 6.2). Spouse carers who were burdened experienced greater negative affect as well as lower positive affect. Among non-spouse caregivers, however, burden was associated only with negative affect as was the case in the total sample.

Overall, this supports the reliability of the newly developed burden measures, and justifies rationalising the dependent measures by combining them into a single burden scale. They not only correlated with each other but they showed a similar pattern of relationships with measures of symptoms and well-being. The combined burden scale had an alpha reliability coefficient of .84, a mean of 28.38 and a standard deviation of 4.11. Scores ranged from 17 to 34.

## Demographic differences in burden

Burden scores were compared for different types of caregivers to find out if some groups were at greater risk than others. Groups were defined in terms of the caregiver–carereceiver relationship (spouse or non-spouse), caregiver gender and age, carereceiver gender and age, and living arrangements (separate or shared). As might have been expected, the demographic variables were not independent of each other (see Table 6.3). Spouse carers tended to be markedly older and their carereceivers were overall younger, male and co-resident. When males cared, they were more likely to be caring for a spouse. The trend was for care to be provided to a person of the opposite gender, due largely to the practice of spouse caring.

**Table 6.3　Correlations among the demographic characteristics ($N=136$)[a]**

| Demographic characteristics | 1 | 2 | 3 | 4 | 5 | 6 |
|---|---|---|---|---|---|---|
| 1 Carer's gender | | | | | | |
| 2 Carer's age | −.23** | | | | | |
| 3 Carereceiver's gender | −.39*** | −.21** | | | | |
| 4 Carereceiver's age | .17* | .01 | .07 | | | |
| 5 Relationship | −.30*** | .73*** | −.37*** | −.39*** | | |
| 6 Residence | −.18* | .22** | −.11 | −.23** | .31*** | |

Notes:　a This is the minimum sample size on which any single correlation is based. The maximum is 144.
　　　　* $p<.05$　　　** $p<.01$　　　*** $p<.001$

Group scores were compared on the component burden scales (disruption and inadequacy) as well as on the total burden scale. Scores on the disruption scale were not found to differ from one group to another. These data suggest that each of the demographic groups was as adversely affected as the others in terms of not getting enough sleep, being constantly on call, not getting through the daily chores, and not having a regular routine. Male carers were affected as much as female carers, co-residents as much as those living apart, spouses as much as non-spouses, and the young as much as the old.

A different pattern emerged, however, when groups were compared on the inadequacy scale. Feelings such as being unable to get on top of things, divided loyalties, guilt, and resentment were more common among caregivers who were young, who were women, and who were involved in non-spouse caregiving.[1]

A stepwise multiple linear regression analysis was carried out, regressing total burden scores on the demographic variables. Although both carer's age and gender correlated significantly with the total burden scores (see Table 6.4), only gender emerged as a significant predictor with a beta weight of .18 ($p<.05$). Gender accounted for 3 per cent of the variance in burden ($F$ [1131] = 4.67, $p<.05$).

**Table 6.4** Correlations of burden ($N=133$) and minor psychiatric symptoms ($N=132$) with the demographic variables

| Demographic variables | Burden | Minor psychiatric symptoms |
|---|---|---|
| Relationship | −.13 | .05 |
| Carer's gender | .19* | .16* |
| Residence | −.01 | .17* |
| Carereceiver's gender | −.09 | −.23** |
| Carer's age | −.16* | −.01 |
| Carereceiver's age | −.04 | −.12 |

Notes: * p<.05    ** p<.01

Having women report higher caregiving burden than men is consistent with much work in the field (Fitting et al., 1986; Gilhooly, 1984; Robinson & Thurnher, 1979; Stephens & Christianson, 1986; Zarit et al., 1986). Separate analyses showed that gender differences arose in relation to the inadequacy measure rather than the disruption measure. Graham (1983) has argued that 'the experience of caring is the medium through which women are accepted into and feel they belong in the social world'. Consequently, women's identity, unlike that of men, is bound up in the caregiving role. Caregiving experiences, however, are not always positive and tying one's identity to caring may not always be beneficial to the caregiver.

Caregiving can impact negatively on a person's identity in so far as the care provided brings neither a cure nor relief. Under circumstances where caring brings frustration and loss, Graham's analysis provides us with an explanation for why women report higher inadequacy scores than men even though they do not report greater disruption in their lives. Giving care does not entail more work for women, but it does mean more to them personally. This interpretation of the data is consistent with Robinson and Thurnher's (1979) observation that men were more able to distance themselves from the emotional upheavals and the guilt that many women experienced in the caregiving role.

### Minor psychiatric symptoms

The burden measure has provided a picture of a group for whom caregiving is a serious threat to quality of life. This picture is reinforced by a closer analysis of the minor psychiatric symptoms which the same carers reported on the DSSI/sAD and the 4-NS.

On the DSSI/sAD, caregivers' scores ranged from 0 to 35 with a mean of 7.05 ($SD = 6.94$). According to Bedford et al.'s (1976) criteria, cases scoring 6 or more can be considered pathological. Forty-seven per cent of caregivers fell into this category. Comparative data on the DSSI/sAD were available from Henderson et al.'s (1981) community sample of 243 Canberra adults. When this sample was weighted on age and sex to increase its comparability to the caregiving sample, the magnitude of the difference became readily apparent. The mean for the Canberra sample was 3.08 ($SD = 4.24$) and only 20 per cent received a score which equalled or exceeded 6. The differences in the distributions in Figure 6.1 suggest that care-givers report an alarmingly high number of symptoms of anxiety and depression.

**Figure 6.1    Distribution of scores on the DSSI/sAD among caregivers and a weighted community sample**

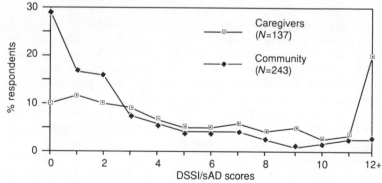

On the 4-NS respondents were asked if, in the last month, they had suffered from any one of 13 symptoms. Four of these symptoms, anxiety, depression, irritability, and nervousness, constituted the 4-NS. Consequently, scores could range from 0 (meaning no symptoms) to 4 (meaning all four symptoms). As can be seen from Figure 6.2, more symptoms were evident in the caregiving sample than in the weighted community sample. Whereas almost half (49 per cent) of the community sample reported no symptoms at all, only 23 per cent of the caregivers were symptom free. The scale mean for the caregiving sample was 1.76 (*SD* = 1.36) compared with .89 (*SD* = 1.12) among the weighted community sample.

**Figure 6.2   Distribution of scores on the 4-NS among caregivers and a weighted community sample**

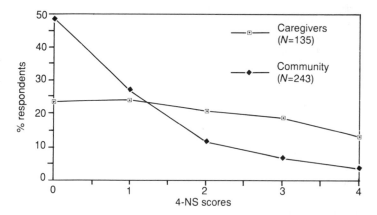

For the purposes of further data analyses in the chapters to follow, the DSSI/sAD and 4-NS scores were combined following the procedure favoured by Henderson et al. (1981). As expected, the measures were very highly correlated with each other ($r$ = .63, $N$ = 134, $p<.001$). Because these two instruments were based on different metrics, scores were standardised and then added. The combined scores ranged from −2.32 to 5.68 with a mean of .02 (*SD* = 1.81).

The combined minor psychiatric symptom scale was related to three demographic variables. Symptoms were higher for carers who were women, who were caring for men, and who were residing with the carereceiver (see Table 6.4). In a stepwise multiple linear regression analysis, one variable dominated the others. Male recipients of care had carers who reported higher levels of anxiety and depression. The gender of the carereceiver had a beta weight of −.23 ($p<.01$) and accounted for a significant 5 per cent of variance in minor psychiatric symptoms ($F$ [1130] = 7.32, $p<.01$). Gilhooly (1984) also has reported greater well-being among the carers of women than the carers of men.

## Conclusion

Burden was found to be very high among caregivers with three-quarters endorsing at least half of the indices of basic need frustration. As expected, burden was related to poor mental health. The psychiatric screening instruments for anxiety and depression provided further evidence of the stress experienced by the caregiving population. Caregivers reported far more symptoms than would have been expected in a community sample matched on age and sex.

When demographic variables were used to predict burden and minor psychiatric symptoms, female caregivers were more likely to report burden and male carereceivers were more likely to have carers experiencing minor psychiatric symptoms. The higher burden scores among women were primarily due to their tendency to feel more inadequate in the caregiving situation. Women's greater identification with the caregiving role combined with the losses experienced in this type of caregiving provide an explanation for why women feel more frustrated in the role than their male counterparts.

The variance explained by the demographic predictors, however, was not great, leaving the vast majority of variation in burden unexplained. In the next chapter, we move on to examine the extent to which the workload of the caregiver can contribute to our understanding of the burden phenomenon.

# 7    Caregiving workload

The most obvious, most measured and most measurable aspects of caregiving involve household tasks and personal care. Disabilities that affect daily functioning create needs for assistance that are met by the caregiver. To view caregiving solely in this way, however, overlooks the fact that the consequences of physical disability can be far reaching for the individual concerned, threatening personal identity and giving rise to previously unrecognised social and emotional needs (Charmaz, 1983; Felton et al., 1984).

In other cases, problems with social and emotional funtioning are not a consequence of physical disability, but constitute the basic problem. Such needs, arising perhaps from the death of a spouse, may not be detected by functional health measures. Caregivers can no more turn their backs on the emotional and social needs of those being cared for than they can on their physical needs. Since carers deal with both the physical and social-psychological problems of the carereceiver, both must be taken into account in an analysis of how workload affects caregiving burden.

**Task-oriented demands**

*Household activities*: Caregivers were asked to indicate whether or not the person being cared for participated in shopping, major and minor meal preparation, light and heavy cleaning, laundering and ironing, minor household repairs, gardening, financial matters, and transport. As can be seen from Figure 7.1, the majority of carereceivers were assisted on all of these dimensions. The activity in which carereceivers were most likely to participate was minor meal preparation—making a cup of tea or preparing a snack (22 per cent).

*Personal care*: Caregivers used a five-point rating scale to indicate the extent to which the carereceiver needed help with such tasks as cutting toenails, combing hair and shaving, dressing and undressing, washing hair, bathing, toileting, getting into and out of bed, sitting and standing, walking, feeding, and taking medication. For Figure 7.2, the data are presented in two categories—help needed and

**Figure 7.1  The percentage of carereceivers (*N*=144) requiring assistance with household activities**

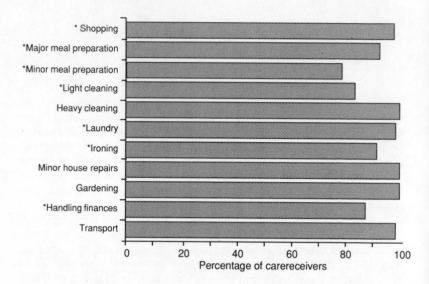

**Figure 7.2  The percentage of carereceivers (*N*=144) requiring assistance with personal care**

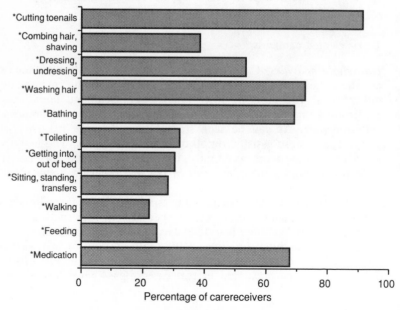

help not needed. As can be seen from this graph, the majority could move freely within the home, feed themselves, go to the toilet, comb their hair, and shave if necessary without assistance or supervision. They were likely to need help, however, with dressing, bathing, medication, washing hair, and cutting toenails.

*Supervision*: The question of supervision was examined by asking caregivers if they left the carereceiver alone unsupervised for a couple of hours first during the day, and second, during the night. Caregivers were also asked if the carereceiver could use the telephone or call for assistance if no one was on hand.

**Figure 7.3   The percentage of carereceivers (*N*=144) requiring supervision**

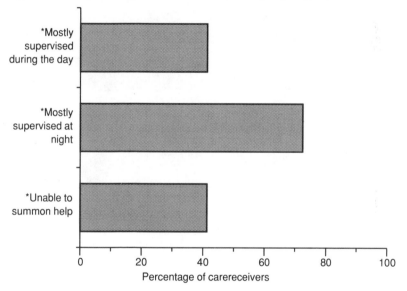

As Figure 7.3 shows, just over half of the carereceivers (58 per cent) were left alone for a short while during the day and were able to summon help if it was required. At night, the majority of caregivers (74 per cent) were rarely separated from the person they were caring for. Reasons given by caregivers for supervision fell into three major categories. The disability or frailty of the carereceiver was an impediment to going out in only 31 per cent of cases. Immobility and falling were frequently mentioned. Carers of dementia sufferers reported instances of their dependants following them or trying unsuccessfully to find them when they went out. For 16 per cent, the disincentive was the carereceiver's distress if the caregiver was absent. According to one caregiver: 'Mother is frightened at night. She gets depressed and cries. She is aware of her vulnerability, she can't defend herself or move as quickly as she could'. Another carer reported how the family was 'blackmailed' into staying at home — 'It's lovely for you. I'll try not to cry' was the reply to any suggestion of an outing for someone else. A further 17 per cent of caregivers felt concerned themselves if they were away for too long, at times with good reasons: 'He calls the police if I'm even five minutes late'. These data clearly illustrate the way in which caregiving activities go beyond the needs that arise directly from disability.

**Figure 7.4    The percentage of carereceivers (*N*=144) requiring assistance with decision making**

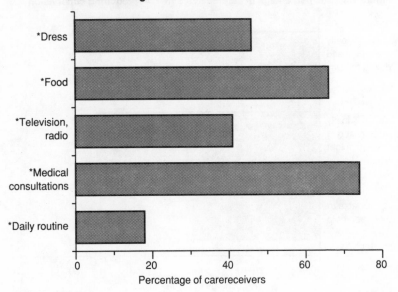

*Decision-making*: Caregivers were asked if the person receiving care made decisions about clothing, food, the daily routine, watching television or listening to the radio, and seeing the doctor (see Figure 7.4). The majority functioned autonomously in these areas, the exceptions being visits to the doctor and food. Doctors themselves usually decided when the next appointment should be. With regard to choice of food, the person preparing the meal also decided on the menu.

*The task-oriented scales*

The household activities, personal care, supervision, and decision-making items were examined in turn with a view to developing four scales to represent each facet of the task-oriented workload. The items comprising the scales are asterisked in Figures 7.1 to 7.4. Intercorrelations, alpha reliability coefficients, means, and standard deviations for the four scales are presented in Table 7.1. All were satisfactory from a psychometric point of view, although caution was warranted with regard to household activities. The variance remained small on this scale, even after eliminating the least discriminating items.

**Table 7.1** **Alpha reliability coefficients (the diagonal), intercorrelations, means, and standard deviations for the house task-oriented scales**

| Task-oriented scales | 1 | 2 | 3 | 4 |
|---|---|---|---|---|
| 1  Household activities | .74 | | | |
| 2  Personal care | .46 | .87 | | |
| 3  Supervision | .38 | .48 | .54 | |
| 4  Decision-making | .33 | .39 | .32 | .68 |
| *M* | 13.28 | 29.78 | 4.57 | 8.95 |
| *SD* | 1.30 | 11.32 | 1.03 | 2.64 |
| *N* | 144 | 144 | 144 | 138 |

Of note is the fact that all scales represent the tasks that are done for the carereceiver. They may not reflect the true needs of the carereceiver, nor do they represent the tasks that the carer actually does. Other family members may help with some chores, community agencies with others. Rather than measuring carereceiver need or caregiver participation, workload is being construed as carers' perceptions of the services provided.

The justification for using such a measure is threefold. First, a caregiver is defined as a person who accepts responsibility for providing care. The responsibility may be exercised by delegating tasks to others or doing the tasks oneself. Responsibility is assumed to be as much a part of the workload as actual task performance. Perceptions of service provision encompass responsibility, whereas data on who provides the service does not. Second, the definition of burden proposed in Chapter 2 hinges on the threat to basic needs posed by caregiving demands. It is therefore important to measure demands separately from the way in which caregivers go about meeting them. Caregiving demands are issues of responsibility. How they are met is a question of the carer's use of personal, social and material resources.

The third consideration was one which rendered the theoretical issues irrelevant to some extent. When the scales were scored in two ways — according to the assistance received and according to caregiver involvement — enormous overlap was found. For the household activities the correlation between the two scales was .72, for personal care .89, and for supervision 1.00. Comparable data were not collected on decision-making. The strength of these correlations suggests that, in practice, perceptions of care (responsibility) and involvement in care (participation) are empirically indistinguishable in this research context.

*Demographic differences on the task-oriented scales*: Household assistance was provided more often by spouse carers, older carers and co-resident carers to carereceivers who were male and younger. Regressing household assistance on the demographic variables using stepwise multiple linear regression analysis resulted in 26 per cent of the variance in assistance being accounted for ($F$ [2133] = 23.09, $p<.001$) by co-residency ($\beta$ = .44, $p<.001$) and whether or not the carereceiver was male ($\beta$ = $-.21$, $p<.01$).

The co-residency finding reflects the fact that a significant proportion of dependants living with caregivers had moved to their caregiver's house. They therefore had fewer obligations with regard to household maintenance. The gender finding can best be explained in terms of traditional roles. Men are less likely to do household chores and are more likely to have others do these tasks for them. From these data it appears that unequal distribution of labour in performing household tasks is not confined to those in good health. Among those in poor health, men still receive more assistance than women. An alternative interpretation of these data—that male carereceivers were less able than female carereceivers—was considered an unlikely explanation. If this were so, a comparable gender difference could have been expected on assistance with personal care. Such was not the case.

Greater personal care requirements were associated with co-residency, and were more likely to involve spouse carers and older carers. When a stepwise multiple linear regression analysis was used, only one significant predictor emerged, whether care was being provided to a spouse or not ($\beta$ = .27, $p<.01$). The variable accounted for 7 per cent of the variance in personal care ($F$ [1134] = 10.31, $p<.01$).

This finding most likely reflects greater severity of handicap in those being cared for by their spouse. It will be recalled that caring for spouses was more likely to result from a specific illness. In particular, stroke was more common in spouse caregiving situations. Therefore, one would expect to find spouse carereceivers needing more help, particularly with dressing, toileting, and getting into and out of bed. These were the tasks on which spouse and non-spouse differences were greatest. A second finding which is consistent with greater need in spouse recipients has already been mentioned in Chapter 4. Spouse carers have a greater commitment to providing care in that they are willing to tolerate a greater degree of disability than other caregivers.

An alternative interpretation which should be mentioned briefly is bias in perception of need. Spouse caregivers may overestimate the assistance required or caregivers to aged parents may underestimate such assistance. Although perceptual bias cannot be ruled out, the explanation would have greater appeal if spouse caring emerged consistently as a major predictor of task-oriented demands.

Supervision was most likely to be given to carereceivers who were younger, who were being cared for by their spouse and who were co-residents. A stepwise multiple linear regression analysis pointed to living arrangements ($\beta = .24$, $p<.01$) and carereceiver's age ($\beta = -.19$, $p<.05$) as the predictors which accounted for most variance in burden, 11 per cent ($F$ [2133] $= 8.44$, $p<.001$).

It is not surprising that those receiving supervision are more likely to be co-residents. Supervision is obviously more readily provided in a shared household and those in need of supervision are more likely to have moved in with their caregivers. Added to this is the likely greater need for supervision among those who were always co-residents — spouse recipients. It has already been noted that spouses provide higher levels of personal care than non-spouses.

Why older recipients should receive less supervisory care is less readily interpreted. If anything, one would have expected the need for supervision to increase with age. The relationship could not be accounted for by other demographic variables, the most obvious of which was whether or not care was being provided by a spouse. Spouse care recipients were younger and spouse carers were more willing to provide intensive levels of care in the home. Maybe the explanation has something to do with the willingness of the carer in conjunction with the availability of alternative forms of care. At the time the study was conducted, nursing home beds were not readily available and the homes had long waiting lists. Carers may have been more successful in obtaining access to nursing home care for the old-old than for the young-old, leaving a more able older population receiving community care.

Decision-making was more often a caregiving responsibility of women, co-residents and those with a male recipient. A stepwise multiple linear regression analysis resulted in the emergence of two significant predictors, the caregiver's gender ($\beta = .26$, $p<.01$) and living arrangements ($\beta = .22$, $p<.01$). The variance in decision-making which was accounted for by these demographic variables was 9 per cent ($F$ [2133] $= 6.86$, $p<.01$).

The greater likelihood of female carers taking on decision-making is consistent with women's traditional nurturant role and with women's greater sense of involvement in caregiving (Graham, 1983).

The importance of living arrangements is likely to stem from the fact that those who cannot make their own decisions are most likely to become co-residents. Not to be dismissed lightly, however, is the notion that co-resident care recipients are a relatively powerless group, who may be given little opportunity to decide for themselves even when they are capable of doing so.

## Conclusion

Although the vast majority of carereceivers needed support with household chores, they varied markedly in the personal care they received (17 per cent were quite independent, 19 per cent highly dependent), supervision (19 per cent received none, 22 per cent were always supervised) and decision-making (32 per cent functioned autonomously, 9 per cent did so rarely).

Three demographic findings were of particular interest. First, men receiving care had more household tasks done for them than women receiving care, despite the fact that both groups appeared to be equally disabled. Whether this reflects more assistance being offered to men (Fitting & Rabins, 1985; Gibson & Allen, 1988), or a greater readiness by men to accept help is unclear from these data. Second, women who cared were more involved in decision-making than men who cared. Yet there was no indication that those being cared for by women were more impaired than those being cared for by men. This is consistent with women being more nurturant than men and also with the notion that women experience greater involvement in the caring role than men. Women's greater sensitivity to changes in the well-being of ageing family members (Lieberman, 1978) may also lead to their doing more than is required. Finally, those cared for by their spouse required more intensive personal care than those being cared for in the community by other relatives. This finding suggests that spouse carers not only speak in terms of greater commitment to the caring role, they act upon it.

## Social-emotional demands

*Social and emotional support*: The social and emotional support given to the carereceiver was assessed by three measures based on items from Henderson et al.'s (1981) Interview Schedule for Social Interaction (ISSI). First, the extent to which the carer was the carereceiver's confidant was assessed. Second, the involvement of others was measured, the justification being that the demands felt by the caregiver would be inversely related to the size of the carereceiver's network of friends.

Data on who the carereceiver relied upon and who else was

a confidant of the carereceiver was obtained through five questions — who the careceivers leant on, who they were close to, who they shared their happiness with, who they shared their most private feelings with, and who comforted them with a hug.[1] From these responses, two scores were calculated, one representing the number of times the caregiver was mentioned as a confidant, the second representing the number of different people who were mentioned as confidants.

The number of times caregivers saw themselves as confidant ranged from 0 to 5 ($M = 2.83$, $SD = 1.60$). Scores were well spread across the distribution. In 24 per cent of cases, the caregivers mentioned themselves only once or not at all, 38 per cent mentioned themselves two or three times, and for a further 38 per cent, the caregiver was the confidant four or five times.

Not surprisingly, carereceivers did not have a large circle of confidants. They ranged in number from 0 to 6 ($M = 2.47$, $SD = 1.15$). It was rare for caregivers to report their recipients as having no confidant (1 per cent), although 20 per cent reported only one, in most cases, themselves. Sixteen per cent of carereceivers were reported to have four or more confidants.

The third measure of the carer's involvement in providing social and emotional support was indirect, like the second, but asked questions about how big a social network the carereceiver had rather than about intimate relationships. Four items were used from the ISSI forming a scale with an alpha reliability coefficient of .62: The number of people the carereceiver had contact with in an ordinary week, the number of people who shared similar interests, the number of friends who could visit and take things as they found them, and the number of people who could be contacted at any time and talked to frankly. Seven was the maximum number of people recorded for any one item.

Scores on the availability of social interaction scale were normally distributed, ranging from 0 to 28 ($M = 13.59$, $SD = 6.76$). The very low scores were obtained in situations where caregivers felt that their dependants were so demented that they were not aware of the presence of others.

Neither the carer-as-confidant scale nor the number of confidants the carereceiver had bore any relationship to the demographic variables. Being the confidant of the carereceiver was no more likely to occur among spouses than non-spouses, with co-residency than separate residency, with female carers than male carers, with female recipients than male recipients, or with carers and recipients of a certain age. Women being cared for, however, had a larger social network ($M = 14.66$, $SD = 6.50$) than men who were being cared for ($M = 12.02$, $SD = 6.88$)[2]; a result which mirrors the well-documented finding that older women have broader social networks than older men (Lowenthal, 1975; Mugford & Kendig, 1986; Wenger, 1984). It remains to be seen whether or not carers invest more time in maintaining the social networks of female dependants or whether these women are themselves responsible for this outcome.

*Maintaining social networks*: Maintaining the social life of the carereceiver was indexed by the extent to which the carer arranged outings suggested either by the person being cared for or the carer. Thirty-five per cent of caregivers arranged outings most times when the carereceiver expressed an interest. In 57 per cent of cases, outings were likely to eventuate when the caregiver took the initiative.

Gender of neither caregiver nor carereceiver affected the effort carers put into maintaining networks. The only significant demographic differences noted involved outings initiated by the person being cared for. Forty-seven per cent of spouses were likely to assist compared with only 26 per cent of non-spouses[3], a finding which is consistent with both the greater commitment of spouses and the competing commitments of non-spouse carers which may prevent involvement. Furthermore, older carereceivers were less likely to successfully initiate outings ($r=-.26$, $N=136$, $p<.001$). This relationship was not explained by a higher proportion of non-obliging non-spouse carers among older age groups. Older carereceivers just seem to be less interested in outings.

### Does workload predict burden and stress?

As seen in Table 7.2, workload bore very little relationship to burden. The only significant correlation to emerge involved the number of confidants which the caregiver perceived the carereceiver as having. This relationship, however, was in the opposite direction to that predicted. As the number of confidants that the carereceiver had increased, so did burden. It seems likely that the work aspect of providing emotional support has been overshadowed by interpersonal relationships.

From the pattern of correlations in Table 7.2, the intimacy of the carereceiver and caregiver relationship is nowhere near as important to burden as the carereceiver having other intimate relationships. One explanation is that sharing confidences with a variety of people may be a way of coping with a carer who is already burdened. If the person being cared for is aware of the carer's frustrations, sharing confidences with outsiders may be an adaptive strategy.

Alternatively, carers may resent the sharing of confidences with others, or feel that sharing such confidences with others represents a vote of no confidence in them as carers. Telling tales featured prominently in some carer's accounts of their difficulties: 'As soon as she is unhappy about something I've done—or usually have not done—she'll say, "Susan will do it for me", and rings my sister to tell her how badly treated she is here.' Carereceivers are powerless to deal with their situation, and an understandable reaction of some was to feel victimised. Unfortunately, and all too often, the only people carereceivers could strike out against were also victims—the powerless carers who had become prisoners of their obligations to care.

**Table 7.2  Correlations of the workload variables with burden and minor psychiatric symptoms (N=125)[a]**

| Workload variables | Burden | Minor psychiatric symptoms |
| --- | --- | --- |
| Task-oriented | | |
| Household activities | .02 | .12 |
| Personal care | −.01 | .05 |
| Supervision | .00 | .24** |
| Decision-making | .08 | −.02 |
| | | |
| Social-emotional | | |
| Carer as confidant | −.01 | −.19* |
| No. confidants | .21** | .08 |
| Availability of social | | |
| interaction | .01 | −.19* |
| Dependant-initiated outings | .02 | −.07 |
| Carer-initiated outings | .14 | .00 |

*Notes:*  a  This is the minimum sample size on which any single correlation is based. The maximum is 134
  \*  $p<.05$    \*\*  $p<.01$

These relationships did not emerge when psychiatric symptoms were used as the outcome measure rather than burden. Three other significant relationships emerged, though they could not be interpreted as evidence of the negative impact workload has on well-being either. As seen in Table 7.2, caregivers with poorer mental health were more likely to perceive the carereceiver as being distant from them, more isolated from outsiders in general and in greater need of supervision. This may be due not to workload, but rather the anguish and grieving associated with watching a loved one deteriorate.

## Is workload important?

From these data, the workload of the caregiver contributes little to understanding either why burden occurs or why mental health is so much at risk in this population. When the task-oriented and social-emotional variables were entered into a stepwise multiple linear regression analysis to predict burden, a significant, though unimpressive, 5 per cent of variance ($F$ [1123] = 5.87, $p<.05$) could be explained by one predictor, the number of confidants of the carereceiver ($\beta$ = .21, $p<.05$). When the same variables were used to predict mental health, 11 per cent of variance was explained ($F$ [2121] = 7.23, $p<.01$) by the need for supervision ($\beta$ = .26, $p<.01$) and by not being the carereceiver's confidant ($\beta$ = $-.22$, $p<.05$).

Not only is the variance accounted for by the workload variables small, but the pattern of correlations suggests that the significant predictors may be reflecting other aspects of the situation. After all, two of the four significant relationships were in the opposite direction to that which was predicted. Interpersonal relationships have been proposed as the explanatory factor in the case of burden. The grieving process associated with degenerative illness such as Alzheimer's Disease is considered likely to underlie the significant relationships found with mental health. Thus, the things that the carer does for the carereceiver, either in terms of physical support or emotional support, bear no direct relationship to the burden and stress of caregiving.

These findings raise important questions about how governments should support community care. Providing essential services such as house cleaning, house repair and meal preparation give elderly people the option of remaining in the community and in this sense their importance is unquestioned. Assistance with workload, particularly that which relieves carers of heavy physical labour, may be essential to preserving the health of the caregiver. However, burden is not a function of the workload of the caregiver, and there is no reason to expect that burden can be controlled by a lightened workload.

# 8 The crises of decline

> The bus came and I watched him walk to the bus. It was like a child leaving for his first day at school—carrying his little bag. It's so distressing. Every morning he asks me, 'What do I do today?'

In Chapter 2, a number of parallels were drawn between providing care for elderly people and providing care for children. Few would deny, however, that there are overriding differences between aged care and child care. The five factors that we identified as the crises of decline commonly confront carers of aged people. Carers of children, except those children with degenerative or terminal illnesses, do not experience such crises.

The five factors that constitute the crisis of decline—awareness of degeneration, unpredictability, time constraints, the caregiver–carereceiver relationship, and lack of choice—have been hypothesised as important contributors to the burden phenomenon.

## Degeneration

Degeneration is used here to refer to the caregiver's perceptions of the physical, social or emotional changes which threaten the individual's social identity. The defining feature is not the extent of the biological deterioration, but the degree to which behaviour is perceived to depart from normal social, emotional and physical functioning. The concern is not with all such behaviours but with changes in the individual which mask the essential features of a person's character or threaten highly valued roles.

Because degeneration is being defined here in terms of its social consequences, problems of measurement are compounded. How does one decide the point at which physical, social and emotional breakdown threatens the social identity of the individual? Different types of deterioration will affect social identity to varying degrees. Individual identities will be differentially affected by a given type of breakdown. Nevertheless, it should be possible to identify a set of core characteristics that indicate loss. An analysis of the early stages of development provides a starting point.

A child learns control over motor coordination, acquires verbal and non-verbal means of communication, and develops social skills in interacting with others. The unpredictable and changeable ways of young children are gradually lost as a unique and organised personality develops, a personality which becomes recognisable to the growing child and to others. Extreme reversal in the acquisition of any of these skills, such as incontinence, immobility, inability to control one's emotions, inability to think coherently, and inconsistency in behaviour, involve loss of control. The individual loses control over physical, social, and emotional functioning which has accrued with maturity. Enduring loss of control is defined as the key concept in degeneration in this study.

**Table 8.1    The degeneration scales and descriptive statistics for scales and items (*N*=138)**

| Scales, statistics, items | % |
| --- | --- |
| Physical deterioration<br>($\alpha$=.71, *M*=4.73, *SD*=1.13) | |
| Lacks mobility | 78 |
| Has trouble controlling bladder | 51 |
| Has trouble controlling bowels | 43 |
| Emotional disturbance<br>($\alpha$=.87, *M*=17.94, *SD*=3.44) | |
| Worries unnecessarily | 78 |
| Wants to be the central concern of your life | 70 |
| Goes on and on about certain things | 69 |
| Constantly demands assistance | 69 |
| Gets very upset, may cry | 68 |
| Is irritable | 67 |
| Gets deeply depressed | 65 |
| Has sudden changes of mood | 61 |
| Is overly critical | 54 |
| Tends to expect the worst all the time | 53 |
| Becomes angry and threatening | 40 |
| Cognitive impairment<br>($\alpha$=.86, *M*=13.71, *SD*=2.96) | |
| Does strange things | 66 |
| Gets off the subject when having a conversation | 64 |
| Gets mixed up about the day, the year | 63 |
| Does not understand what is said | 62 |
| Is not interested in news of friends and relatives | 52 |
| Fails to recognise familiar people and places | 50 |
| Does not respond sensibly when spoken to | 46 |
| Endangers her/himself | 44 |
| Wanders outside the house | 24 |

Degeneration was measured through three scales. Their items and corresponding scale statistics appear in Table 8.1. The first represented physical deterioration and comprised three items measuring incontinence and immobility. Nineteen per cent of carereceivers had none of these problems, while a sizeable 35 per cent had all three of them. The scale mean was 4.73.

The second scale, emotional disturbance, was made up of 11 items which represented depressed mood, lack of emotional control, sudden mood change, and socially inappropriate behaviour toward others. Scores ranged from 11 to 22, but were somewhat skewed, as reflected in the mean of 17.94.

The third scale represented cognitive impairment. The nine items tapped confusion about persons, place, and time, poor knowledge, and poor communication capacity. Scores were normally distributed, ranging from 9 to 18 with a mean of 13.71.

These scales showed moderate relationships with each other: .22 ($N=134$, $p<.01$) between physical deterioration and cognitive impairment, .27 ($N=132$, $p<.001$) between physical deterioration and emotional disturbance, and .48 ($N=132$, $p<.001$) between emotional disturbance and cognitive impairment. Scores on the three degeneration scales did not differ across demographic groups, though all were strongly related to burden. High burden was reported by carers who saw signs of substantial physical deterioration, emotional disturbance and cognitive impairment in the person they were caring for. In a stepwise multiple linear regression, 32 per cent of variance in the burden measure was accounted for ($F$ [2128] $= 29.74$, $p<.001$), the major predictors being emotional disturbance ($\beta = .43$, $p<.001$) and cognitive impairment ($\beta = .21$, $p<.01$). Physical deterioration did not contribute anything above and beyond that explained by the other scales.

**Table 8.2  Correlations of the degeneration scales with burden and minor psychiatric symptoms ($N=129$)[a]**

| Degeneration scales | Burden | Minor psychiatric symptoms |
| --- | --- | --- |
| Physical deterioration | .30*** | .08 |
| Emotional disturbance | .53*** | .25** |
| Cognitive impairment | .42*** | .25** |

Notes: a This is the minimum sample size on which any single correlation is based. The maximum is 134.
** $p<.01$      *** $p<.001$

Seeing the carereceiver's intellect and personality degenerate were also linked with minor psychiatric symptoms in the carer (see Table 8.2). Of interest was the finding that while mental health appeared to be adversely affected by personality and cognitive changes, no relationship emerged between mental health and physical changes. It seems that 'loss of a person' is a more difficult thing for carers to endure than observing decrements in the physical functioning of a loved one (Lezak, 1978).

These results are open to another interpretation. All data come from the same source—the caregiver. Is it possible that a caregiver who is anxious and depressed will see the carereceiver's behaviour more negatively because of his or her own mood? In such an event, the observed social and emotional behaviour of the person being cared for would be more vulnerable to distortion than physical behaviour. This would account for why the social and emotional behaviour scales correlated with psychiatric symptoms, while the physical behaviour scale did not.

**Table 8.3   Standardised linear regression coefficients and R² values for two models predicting burden (N=129)**

| Predictors | Model 1 | Model 2 |
|---|---|---|
| Minor psychiatric symptoms | .43 | .29*** |
| Emotional disturbance | | .38*** |
| Cognitive impairment | | .16 |
| R² | .19*** | .40*** |
| R² change | | .21*** |

*Notes:*   ***   *p*<.001

In order to examine the extent to which mood state might account for the association between emotional disturbance and cognitive impairment and burden, a hierarchical regression model was set up in which symptoms were entered into the equation first. As can be seen from Table 8.3, controlling for mood made little impact on the relationship between degeneration and burden. An additional and substantial 21 per cent of variance was accounted for by the degeneration scales ($F$ [2125] = 21.88, *p*<.001).

**Unpredictability**

The extent to which caregivers were prepared for the caregiving role was assessed through four separate questions. Caregivers were asked 1) how much they knew about the carereceivers' problems when they began to care; 2) how much they had to learn about providing care; 3) how suddenly they were thrown into the caregiving role; and 4) whether caregiving involved unexpected adverse changes in the carereceiver's condition. Carers' responses divided surprisingly evenly on these questions. A slight majority, 57 per cent, knew quite a lot about the carereceiver's condition when they first provided care, 51 per cent had things to learn about caring and 52 per cent became involved suddenly rather than gradually. Forty per cent reported unexpected deterioration in the carereceiver's condition. Thus, although a sizeable group had to cope with unpredictability in the caregiving role, they were by no means the overwhelming majority. Related to unpredictability is the question of how long carers had been caring. One might expect that those who had been caregivers longest would have experienced more unpredictability. Furthermore, they would be more aware of the way in which caring can occupy decades rather than a few short years. While the mean number of years for which caring had been provided was 5.52, the variability was enormous, ranging from 0 to 45 years ($SD = 6.66$).

The indices of unpredictability did not vary across demographic groups, with two exceptions. First, older carers were less knowledgeable about the condition of the person they were caring for than younger carers ($r=-.20$, $N=136$, $p<.05$), reflecting perhaps better consumer education on medical matters in younger generations. Second, carers looking after people who were younger were more likely to be thrown into the caregiving role suddenly ($r=-.21$, $N=144$, $p<.01$), a finding consistent with the greater prevalence of sudden onset conditions, such as stroke, among this group.

**Table 8.4  The correlations of the unpredictability variables with burden and minor psychiatric symptoms ($N=132$)[a]**

| Unpredictability indices | Burden | Minor psychiatric symptoms |
|---|---|---|
| Knowledge | −.18* | −.22** |
| Learning | .31*** | .18* |
| Unexpected onset | .09 | .11 |
| Unexpected degeneration | .17* | .20* |
| Years caring | .02 | −.06 |

Notes:  a This is the minimum sample size on which any single correlation is based. The maximum is 135.
* $p<.05$   ** $p<.01$   *** $p<.001$

Three of the five unpredictability indices were related to both burden and minor psychiatric symptoms (see Table 8.4). High burden and symptoms accompanied poor knowledge initially, having to learn a great deal about caring, and observing unexpected degeneration in the carereceiver.

When the three significant predictors were entered into a stepwise multiple linear regression analysis, only the amount which had to be learnt emerged as a significant predictor of burden ($\beta = .31$, $p<.001$), accounting for 10 per cent of the variance ($F$ [1131] = 14.30, $p<.001$). With regard to symptoms, knowledge of the carereceiver's condition was the major predictor ($\beta = -.22$, $p<.05$), accounting for 5 per cent of the variance in the criterion ($F$ [1130] = 6.37, $p<.05$).

Of interest is the absence of relationships involving either unexpected onset or years spent caring. It seems that having the necessary knowledge and experience are the important factors rather than having some certainty about the future. The unexpectedness of caregiving is thus more of a threat to the carer's self-esteem than to any need for order and stability in life.

At the same time, some care is warranted in interpreting the relationship between years caring and burden or symptoms. As was mentioned earlier, local nursing homes had lengthy waiting lists at the time this study was conducted and most carers had their carereceivers' names on these lists as insurance for the future. A substantial proportion of carers, after a period of time, were therefore likely to be given the option of nursing home care. One would expect families who were greatly burdened to accept the offer, thus removing long-term burdened caregivers from the sample.

### Time constraints

The extent to which the competing obligations of caregivers contributed to burden and poor mental health was assessed through both objective and subjective indices. The four objective measures were whether or not the caregiver had: 1) three generations in the one household, 2) children under 16 years of age, 3) a spouse who was not the carereceiver, and 4) employment outside the home. Caregivers' perceptions of the constraints on their time because of caregiving constituted the subjective index. The time constraints scale had an alpha reliability coefficient of .79 and comprised 5 items: 1) missing out on outings and holidays, 2) having to plan any outing or holiday well in advance, 3) having less time to spend with the rest of the family, 4) having so little time to yourself, and 5) giving up interests, leisure activities or hobbies. The scale was highly skewed with the vast majority of caregivers experiencing such restrictions. Although scores ranged from 5 to 10, the mean was 9.10 ($SD$ = 1.41).

As expected, the objective indices varied across demographic groups, in particular, across spouse and non-spouse caring and carers' age. Forty-six per cent of non-spouse carers had three generation households compared to only 2 per cent of spouse carers, 28 per cent of non-spouse carers had children under 16 years of age compared with only 2 per cent of spouse carers, 43 per cent of non-spouse carers had work outside the home compared with only 10 per cent of spouse carers, and 72 per cent of non-spouse carers had to find time for their own spouse.[1] Furthermore, younger carers were more likely to have three-generation households ($r=-.52$, $N=137$, $p<.001$), additional commitments to children under 16 ($r=.-53$, $N=137$, $p<.001$), work ($r=-.48$, $N=137$, $p<.001$) and a spouse ($r=-.62$, $N=137$, $p<.001$).

These results suggest that problems of time constraints depend to a considerable degree on the carer's stage of life. Of some surprise, therefore, was the finding that these differences did not flow over to affect subjective reports of time constraints. Older carers and spouse carers were no less likely to experience time constraints than younger carers and non-spouse carers. One explanation arises from the extraordinarily high endorsement rate for items in the time constraints scale. When carers see the person they are caring for not coping, they may concentrate all their energies on maximising this person's comfort, disregarding other family members, leisure, hobbies, and relaxation. In other words, caregiving consumes all the time carers have available and then more, intruding on other commitments regardless of whether they are numerous or few. Caregiving had become the total preoccupation of some of the carers interviewed. When asked what she would miss if she wasn't caregiving, one spouse caregiver replied, 'It's a funny thing to have to answer . . . It's your whole life'.

Table 8.5 Correlations of the competing commitments variables with burden and minor psychiatric symptoms

| Competing commitments | Non-spouse ($n=73$)[a] | | Total ($N=127$)[a] | |
|---|---|---|---|---|
| | Burden | Minor psychiatric symptoms | Burden | Minor psychiatric symptoms |
| Three generations | .14 | −.02 | | |
| Children < 16 | .15 | .22* | | |
| Marriage | .01 | .08 | | |
| Employment | −.12 | −.04 | −.02 | −.09 |
| Time constraints | .54*** | .25* | .52*** | .21** |

Notes: a These are the minimum sample sizes on which the correlations are based. The maximum sample sizes are 78 for non-spouse carers and 134 for total carers.
  * $p<.05$      ** $p<.01$      *** $p<.001$

Only the sample of non-spouse carers could sensibly be used to ascertain whether or not burden was related to three of the objective variables (having a three-generation household, children under 16, a spouse who was not the carereceiver). These factors had no direct effect on burden, though having young children or teenagers was associated with more reports of anxiety or depression among carers (see Table 8.5). Whether or not this has anything to do with caring for an older person, however, is not clear. Just as other commitments in the home did not exacerbate burden, neither did commitments outside the home. Workforce participation was not associated with any signs of stress among caregivers.

In contrast, the subjective measure proved to be highly related to both burden and symptoms. Finding that objective measures of time pressure could not explain burden while subjective measures could has important ramifications for the way in which burden is conceptualised. The results reinforce the view that burden is a subjective phenomenon. One might argue that this test is not fair, since burden was defined subjectively at the outset. The argument is difficult to sustain, however, when attention is turned to the analyses which used a combination of two psychiatric screening instruments as the criterion variable. Minor psychiatric symptoms are assessed not merely through feelings of well-being but through reports of behaviour. Furthermore, symptoms cannot be dismissed lightly in that they are central to cost-benefit analyses of the feasibility of home care. There is little to be gained, for instance, in cutting aged care expenditure on one hand and increasing health care expenditure for carers on the other. With the more 'hard-core' outcome variable of symptoms, the subjective measure of time constraints again was the major predictor. The one objective indicator which was related to symptoms, having children under 16 years, could not add significantly to the variance accounted for by the time constraints scale.

## The caregiver–carereceiver relationship

Research on parental influences in the development of neurosis suggests that two styles of interaction are important to later adjustment: the degree of affection parents show their children and the degree of autonomy they allow their children (Parker, 1978). These past styles of interacting were considered to have a likely influence on the way in which parent and child related to each other in the caregiving situation. The expectation was that high burden would be experienced when there had been a history of the carer receiving a great deal of affection, very little affection[2] and little autonomy. High affection was expected to exacerbate the sense of loss associated with caregiving, little affection was expected to arouse feelings of rejection in the caregiver, while little autonomy was expected to result in battles of control which could threaten the carer's sense of competence. From interviews with caregivers, issues of past affection and autonomy seemed as relevant to spouse caring situations as to parent–child situations and so the argument was extended to include all carers.

In addition to considering the past relationship between caregiver and carereceiver, questions were asked concerning the quality of the present relationship. As discussed in Chapter 3, recent studies using general measures of relationship quality have tended to produce fairly disappointing results. Consequently, the questions used here were more focused, dealing specifically with interpersonal conflict and appreciation.

The scales of affection and autonomy were adaptations of those devised by Parker (1978). The eight-item affection scale ($\alpha$ = .83) tapped the degree of support, understanding and affection received from the person being cared for in the past. Scores ranged from 8 to 32 with a mean of 23.33 ($SD$ = 6.10). The eight-item autonomy scale ($\alpha$ = .84) covered the amount of independence the carer had been given by the carereceiver in decision-making and choosing courses of action, and how much confidence the carereceiver had shown in the carer's judgement in the past. Scores ranged from 8 to 32 with a mean of 24.09 ($SD$ = 6.01). The correlation between the affection and autonomy scales was .33 ($N$=123, $p$<.001). The scales appear in Appendix 1. In some cases, caregivers did not have a sufficiently long-standing relationship with the carereceiver to complete this section of the questionnaire. Of the 137 respondents who completed the study, 123 were able to answer the past relationship questions.

Present interpersonal conflict was measured on a three-point rating scale by asking carers about differences of opinion with the person they were caring for. Caregivers indicated the level of friction by the response categories hardly ever (1), sometimes (2) or a lot of the time (3). Over a third said hardly ever (39 per cent), just under a third sometimes (31 per cent) and slightly less than a third a lot of the time (30 per cent).

Carers' perceptions of how much their efforts were appreciated by carereceivers were measured by the reciprocity scale. Caregivers were asked how often the carereceiver: 1) told or showed the caregiver that the efforts were appreciated and not taken for granted, 2) gave small gifts to the caregiver or the caregiver's family, and 3) had a chat which cheered up the caregiver. Carers responded to each quesion on a three-point scale with 1 representing rarely, 2 sometimes, and 3 regularly. The alpha reliability coefficient for the scale was .49, somewhat lower than expected. The reciprocity scale scores ranged from 3 to 9 and were normally distributed with a mean of 5.98 ($SD$ = 1.76).

Demographic differences were observed on all of the relationship variables except present interpersonal conflict. Spouse carers and older carers reported receiving more affection from the carereceiver in the past. In a stepwise multiple linear regression analysis, being a spouse carer proved to be the major predictor ($\beta$ = .22, $p$<.05), accounting for 5 per cent of the variance in the criterion ($F$ [1118] = 5.79, $p$<.05).

Autonomy in the past relationship was highest for carers of

spouses and for carers who were male, older and co-residents. In a stepwise multiple linear regression analysis, the one significant predictor to emerge was living arrangements ($\beta = .21$, $p<.05$), accounting for 4 per cent of variance in the criterion ($F$ [1119] = 5.54, $p<.05$). Finding that co-resident carers reported greater autonomy suggests that 'intimacy at a distance' is a stronger guiding principle for some carers than others. Carers who perceived their dependant as having dominated them in the past were more likely to want to keep the person they were caring for in separate living quarters. 'We had to put a lock on our side of the door [between granny flat and house]', said one carer 'otherwise she'd [mother] come straight in...She's a very domineering woman. She doesn't like me to entertain without inviting her...I would miss her if she wasn't there, it's just I don't like her there all the time.' For this carer a self-contained unit for mother was 'essential' and a lock on the carer's side, 'absolutely necessary'.

Reciprocity scores were significantly higher when women were receiving care ($M=6.21$, $SD=1.85$) than when men were ($M=5.60$, $SD=1.55$).[3] The greater appreciation which women show their caregivers may explain Gilleard et al.'s (1984a) finding that older men are more difficult to care for in one's home than older women. Greater appreciation from female dependants, however, did not explain the earlier result that carers of men had more psychiatric symptoms than carers of women.

When the variables assessing the past and present social and emotional bond were related to burden and mental health, three significant relationships emerged (see Table 8.6). High burden was more likely among caregivers who reported relatively little autonomy in their relationship in the past and high conflict in the present situation. The occurrence of conflict also was linked with poor mental health.

**Table 8.6**  **The correlations of the caregiver–carereceiver relationship variables with burden and minor psychiatric symptoms ($N=119$)[a]**

| Caregiver–carereceiver relationship | Burden | Minor psychiatric symptoms |
|---|---|---|
| Affection | −.06 | −.13 |
| Autonomy | −.23** | −.11 |
| Conflict | .21** | .19* |
| Reciprocity | −.09 | −.13 |

*Notes:*  a This is the minimum sample size on which any single correlation is based. The maximum is 134.

  *  $p<.05$      **  $p<.01$

When lack of autonomy in the past and frequency of conflict in the present were entered into a stepwise multiple linear regression analysis, only the autonomy scale emerged as a significant predictor of burden ($\beta = -.23$) accounting for 5 per cent of the variance ($F$ [1119] $= 6.83$, $p<.01$). This was not surprising since past autonomy and current conflict correlated significantly with each other ($r=-.36$, $N=121$, $p<.001$). These data show that conflict represents one aspect of the caregiver–carereceiver relationship which is important in understanding burden and that the grounds for conflict may have their roots in the caregiver's perceptions of past struggles for independence. Furthermore, the absence of any kind of relationship, either nonlinear as predicted or linear, between burden and affection highlights the considerable degree of commitment carers have to their task. Neither the absence of past affection nor the absence of current gratitude led carers to cry burden.

## Lack of choice

The issue of lack of choice was addressed by asking caregivers if they felt able and willing to continue in the role of caregiver. Questions concerning choice in taking on the role in the first place proved more complex than expected. It was difficult for either carer or interviewer to ascertain how much choice was involved. For a substantial number of caregivers, the choice, if it could be called that, was passive. It wasn't the case that they wanted to be the carer. They cared because no one else was willing, able or offered.

Four indices were used to reflect restrictions of choice. The first and most direct asked carers if their dependants were on a nursing home waiting list, and if so, would they accept the offer of a place today if it were made. Approximately 13 per cent of caregivers were both on a waiting list and would have accepted the offer immediately. They wanted to relinquish the caregiving role as soon as possible.

The remaining three indices reflected attitudes to caregiving: What would carers miss if they had to give up caring, for how long did they intend to provide care, and was there a point beyond which they could not care at home. A small proportion of caregivers (17 per cent) were unable to think of anything positive about caregiving. Their typical reply was, 'I'd miss nothing'. Probes relating to companionship, being busy, useful or having someone else in the house failed to initiate a positive response among these respondents. Limitations on how long care would be provided willingly were expressed again by the minority (35 per cent). The majority, however, acknowledged having a breaking point beyond which they would be unable to care (61 per cent).

Two major demographic differences in issues of choice were noted. Spouse and non-spouse caregivers indicated markedly different levels of willingness to care, as discussed in Chapter 5. Those who were caring for someone other than a spouse were more likely to accept an institutional placement (23 per cent compared with 7 per cent for spouse carers), more able to articulate specific limitations on how much care they were prepared to provide (56 per cent compared with 13 per cent) and more aware of having a breaking point (76 per cent compared with 39 per cent).[4]

Having a breaking point was also mentioned by 69 per cent of women compared with only 38 per cent of men.[5] This finding could not be attributed to other demographic variables, and revives earlier discussion about gender differences in caregiving. It is consistent with the higher burden reported by women, but the question of why this is the case remains. Are male caregivers more resilient, are they less likely to push themselves to their limits to become aware of a breaking point, or are they more strongly motivated to present a positive image of themselves in the caregiving role? This issue will be taken up in more detail in Chapter 11.

Table 8.7    **The correlations of choice restriction variables with burden and minor psychiatric symptoms ($N$=127)[a]**

| Choice restrictions | Burden | Minor psychiatric symptoms |
|---|---|---|
| Acceptance of alternative | .24** | .24** |
| Nothing good about it | .06 | .16* |
| Caregiving limit | .21** | .09 |
| Capacity limit | .27*** | .08 |

Notes:   a   This is the minimum size on which any single correlation is based. The maximum is 133.

     *   $p<.05$          **   $p<.01$          ***   $p<.001$

The hypothetical acceptance of a nursing home offer was related to burden as expected (see Table 8.7). Burden was also related to reluctance to continue in the caregiving role. Those who put a limit on how long they would care and saw a limit in their own capacity were more likely to be highly burdened. These variables were entered into a stepwise multiple linear regression analysis. As predictors of burden, they explained 11 per cent of the variance ($F$ [2125] = 7.79, $p<.001$), with significant beta weights emerging for whether or not the carer had a breaking point ($\beta = .23$, $p<.01$) and whether or not the carer would accept a nursing home placement ($\beta = .20$, $p<.05$).

With regard to minor psychiatric symptoms, wanting a nursing home placement emerged as a significant correlate, but specifying a limit on care did not. Possibly the explanation for these findings lies in the extremeness of the attitudinal measures. Specifying limits on one's capacity to care or on the behaviour which would be tolerated in the carereceiver are far more moderate expressions of unwilling-ness than wanting immediate nursing home admission. From this perspective, specifying limits is more likely to correlate with per-ceptions of threat than emergence of symptoms.

The prediction of minor psychiatric symptoms using a stepwise multiple linear regression analysis yielded only one variable with a significant beta weight, nursing home acceptance ($\beta = .24$, $p<.01$). The variable accounted for 6 per cent of variance in the criterion ($F$ [1130] = 8.30, $p<.01$).

In interpreting these data, problems of temporal ordering are more pronounced than anywhere else. For instance, it is just as likely that burden leads to unwillingness and limitations on future care as it is that unwillingness and limitations give rise to burden. Questioning about the choice of a carer could have provided some insights here if the data had been scorable on a choice restriction dimension. Since it was not, the question of which comes first, unwillingness or burden, can only be answered through further prospective research. One might expect, however, that the most appropriate causal model would not be one-way but rather two-way, with unwillingness increasing burden and burden increasing un-willingness.

### Conclusion

The crises of decline could all be linked to some degree with burden and poor mental health among caregivers. The only notable excep-tion involved the time constraint measures. Being a wife, mother or worker as well as a carer did not appear to put carers at greater risk of burden, as was expected. However, the subjective index of time constraints performed quite differently. Carers who saw themselves as having sacrificed leisure activities, time with the family, holidays and outings were at risk of burden and poor mental health.

The crisis of degeneration was unequivocally linked with burden and minor psychiatric symptoms. Carers were particularly vulner-able when faced with emotional or cognitive degeneration in the carereceiver. They were also at risk when they were unprepared for caregiving through lack of knowledge, experience or unexpected deterioration in the person they were caring for. Carers' lack of competence appeared to be the important aspect of unpredictability rather than simply not knowing what was ahead. Unwillingness to care was also linked to burden and symptoms. Those who conceded limitations to the amount of care they would and could provide and those who wanted nursing home support immediately were far more likely to see their basic needs threatened by caregiving.

The fifth crisis examined in this chapter was the social and emotional bond between the caregiver and carereceiver. The data clearly demonstrated that while the negative aspects of interpersonal relationships were important, the positive aspects were not. Affection and appreciation appeared to have nothing to do with whether the carer was burdened, anxious or depressed. The major determinant was whether or not there was conflict in the relationship. As far as burden was concerned, this conflict was associated with a past history of tension. Carers who were burdened were more likely to perceive their dependant as someone who dominated them, overprotected them, and told them what to do.

The crises of decline are very relevant to both caregiving burden and reports of minor psychiatric symptoms in carers. While these data do not allow us to test the theoretical proposition that the crises cause burden, they do provide a firm basis for refocusing our efforts to understand burden. Burden and mental ill health are not products of the physical demands made on carers but are associated with the psychological deficits of caregiving—watching a loved one lose the sense of self, not knowing how to provide care, fighting with the carereceiver for control, being unable to attend to anything else, and 'wanting out'.

Caregiving has been referred to as a labour of love (Finch & Groves, 1982; Graham, 1983). The expression highlights the two dimensions of caregiving—what a carer does and what a carer feels. Carers provide services to the person they are caring for, but not in a detached manner. They also feel a sense of involvement. But this is not always a positive experience. Instead of emotions of love, carers can feel emotions of fear, frustration and pain. They are involved in their caregiving as society dictates they should be, yet their work goes unrewarded. They see a future of further degeneration, further crises, further involvement and further arguments with no other options in sight. Herein lies the burden of care. Caring is no longer a labour of love. Caring becomes a labour of loss.

# 9 Personal resources

As seen in the previous chapter, the crises of decline proved to have an important role to play in understanding burden. This is not to say, however, that there are not other factors contributing to caregiving burden. Individual resources differ—of the personal, social and material kind. In the personal domain, carers have different levels of tolerance as well as different styles for dealing with caregiving problems. Suitability and adaptability to caregiving are examined in this chapter through three characteristics—personality, health and coping strategies.

## Personality

Personality was conceptualised in terms of traits and values which describe the ways in which individuals characteristically perceive, evaluate and interact with the world. The traits considered relevant were self-esteem and mastery, which have been regarded as vulnerability factors in the stress literature, and three components of temperament, namely activity, sociability and emotionality (Buss & Plomin, 1975). The sixth characteristic considered to be relevant was the value placed on kindness, the caregiver's belief that concern for others should be given priority as a guiding principle in life.

Self-esteem, or a person's judgement of his or her own worthiness (Coopersmith, 1967), was measured by adapting Rosenberg's (1965) ten-item scale. The items reflected beliefs about one's worth, competence and capacity for success. The related concept of mastery was used to refer to what some have called an internal locus of control (Levenson, 1981; Rotter, 1966). The mastery scale was intended to gauge the extent to which people believed they had control over their own lives and over the difficulties that beset them. The scale was based on the work of Pearlin and Schooler (1978), the major modification being the balancing of positively and negatively worded items.

The activity, sociability and emotionality scales were based on the EASI-III Temperament Survey (Braithwaite, 1987; Braithwaite et al., 1984; Buss & Plomin, 1975). The eight items in the activity scale were concerned with keeping busy, doing things with vigour and having lots of energy. The five-item sociability scale measured enjoying the company of others. The 15-item emotionality scale reflected the tendency to be readily upset, fearfulness, anger, and impulsiveness. The five personality characteristics mentioned so far were assessed in one self-completion questionnaire in which caregivers described the sort of person they were by rating each question on a scale from very unlike me (1) to very like me (5).

The sixth measure, the kindness scale, was taken from a measure of personal values (Braithwaite & Law, 1985) and comprised four items: being tolerant, helpful, forgiving, and generous. Each item was rated on a four-point scale ranging from not usually valued (1) to valued very highly (4). The items, means and standard deviations for the six personality scales as well as their intercorrelations and alpha reliability coefficients appear in Appendixes 2 and 3.

*Demographic differences in personality*

Only three demographic differences were observed with these personality scales. Female carers obtained higher scores than male carers on sociability ($M=17.04$, $SD=4.27$ compared with $M=15.01$, $SD=4.00$ respectively)[1] and kindness ($M=13.29$, $SD=2.06$ compared with $M=12.41$, $SD=2.49$ respectively)[2]. Both findings are consistent with the more nurturing role of women. Older carers tended to be less emotional than younger carers ($r=-.20$, $N=133$, $p<.01$), though why this relationship should occur is unclear.

Of particular interest was the absence of significant differences between spouse and non-spouse caregivers. If personality was a major factor in the selection of a caregiver, one might have expected differences between these two groups. Monogamy rules out any selection process when care is provided by a spouse. Greater choice, however, is associated with being a non-spouse caregiver, in that siblings are generally available who are just as eligible for the role. In such circumstances, one might have expected a selection bias toward siblings who are personally better suited to caregiving, a bias which would differentiate them from spouses who have no choice. The data fail to support this hypothesis, but a note of caution is warranted. By sampling only caregivers, the influence of personality may have been lost. Comparisons with those who have avoided caregiving responsibilities altogether may lead to different conclusions regarding the role of personality in the selection of carers.

*Personality and burden*

Three of the six personality characteristics were related to burden (see Table 9.1) and all three were highly related to each other (see Appendix 3). High burden was linked with having low self-esteem, little sense of mastery, and being highly emotional. When the personality variables were entered into a stepwise multiple linear regression analysis, two significant predictors emerged, self-esteem ($\beta = -.22$, $p<.05$) and emotionality ($\beta = .20$, $p<.05$). Together they accounted for 13 per cent of the variance ($F$ [2120] = 8.71, $p<.001$). Once these variables were in the equation, beliefs about control over one's life could not contribute anything more to predicting burden.

**Table 9.1 Correlations of the personality scales with burden and minor psychiatric symptoms ($N$=126)[a]**

| Personality scales | Burden | Minor psychiatric symptoms |
|---|---|---|
| Self-esteem | −.30*** | −.41*** |
| Mastery | −.25** | −.50*** |
| Activity | −.06 | −.36*** |
| Sociability | .00 | −.02 |
| Kindness | −.06 | −.14 |
| Emotionality | .29*** | .59*** |

*Notes:* a This is the minimum sample size on which any single correlation is based. The maximum is 133.

** $p<.01$ *** $p<.001$

Doubts were raised in Chapter 2 as to whether those who saw themselves as having complete control over their lives were suited to the often restrictive caregiving situation. From the regression analysis, the variance in the mastery scale which was relevant to burden also appeared in the self-esteem scale. An analysis of the items in each scale led to the conclusion that this common ground represented confidence in one's ability to overcome life's problems. The other facets of controllability—beliefs about the causes of life's problems and a desire to control one's environment—do not appear to be relevant to the experience of burden.

### Personality and minor psychiatric symptoms

The correlates of minor psychiatric symptoms were the same as those of burden with one addition, activity. Low activity was associated with the presence of symptoms. When the symptoms variable was regressed on these personal characteristics, emotionality ($\beta = .46$, $p<.001$) and mastery ($\beta = -.30$, $p<.001$) emerged as the significant predictors accounting for 42 per cent of the variance ($F$ [2120] = 43.00, $p<.001$). Neither self-esteem nor activity added further variance to the regression equation.

The relationship of emotionality and mastery to psychiatric symptoms is consistent with the notion that some personality traits are vulnerability factors for neurosis (Costa & McCrae, 1980; Henderson et al., 1981; Kobasa, 1979). However, the major distinction between emotionality (the tendency to be easily aroused) and psychiatric symptoms (feeling depressed, anxious) is that the former is a general stable disposition (a trait) and the latter is a more transient response (a state). In the caregiving context, the state–trait distinction may be especially blurred. The personality measures are likely to be influenced by the caregiver's levels of anxiety and depression. Where poor mental health is a function of months of caregiving and spans a considerable period of time, caregivers may be unable to recall feeling anyway other than emotional, worthless, out of control, and without energy. Their present perceptions may obliterate their picture of the sort of person they used to be.

### Is personality a better predictor than symptoms?

To examine whether anxiety and depression were distinguishable from enduring personality characteristics in this study, the following question was asked: Do personality traits contribute anything more than psychiatric symptoms to the prediction of burden? A hierarchical multiple regression model was set up to investigate whether the trait measures of emotionality, self-esteem, and mastery would add any variance after psychiatric symptoms had been entered into the equation. They did not. Psychiatric symptoms accounted for 8 per cent of the variance, and the personality traits only accounted for a further non-significant 2 per cent. It seems that we are unable to disentangle symptoms from personality in this data set, which was obtained from caregivers at a point in time well into the caregiving experience.

### Can personality explain burden?

Conclusive evidence of personality predisposing some carers to burden more than others was not forthcoming. Sociability and activity showed no sign of being important predictors of burden. In contrast, emotionality, self-esteem and mastery were significantly related to burden, but they could not be satisfactorily differentiated from psychiatric symptoms. In the absence of unique predictive variance in the trait measures, no claims can be made about the importance of enduring personality characteristics. This finding leads to two questions. Does burden come about because carers do not have either the confidence in themselves or the emotional temperament to withstand stress? Or does burden rob carers of their confidence and equanimity?

### Health

The health problems of caregivers undoubtedly can reduce capacity to provide care. So too can caregivers' beliefs about their health.

Although such beliefs may not be in accord with a medical diagnosis, they are regarded as potentially important predictors of caregiving burden. Beliefs about health problems are expected to make the caregiver feel vulnerable when exposed to caregiving demands, in much the same way as personality was thought to place some individuals at greater risk of burden than others.

Carers were asked to describe their health on a three-point scale: generally good (1), fair (2) or poor (3). The majority (58 per cent) reported their health to be good. A further 33 per cent described their health as fair and only 9 per cent as poor. When enquiries were made about specific health problems, 29 per cent mentioned complaints associated with the muscular-skeletal system (mainly back problems and arthritis), 28 per cent mentioned heart-circulatory problems (mainly blood pressure and hypertension), and 18 per cent reported conditions of a pyschiatric-neurological nature (mainly anxiety, depression, headaches).

Although the majority of caregivers were in good health, comparative data suggest that they may have more problems than found in the general population. In Henderson et al.'s (1981) community sample, a four-point self-report rating scale was used to assess health—very good, good, fair, and poor. A direct comparison with this sample is made difficult by the slightly different rating scale and by the disproportionate number of older women in the carer's sample. To increase comparability, the community sample was weighted on age and sex. In the weighted community sample, 25 per cent described their health as fair or poor, compared with 42 per cent in the carer sample.

## Demographic differences in perceptions of health

Older caregivers were expected to have more health problems than younger caregivers. However, no significant difference was found on self-rated health, although more heart and circulatory problems were mentioned by older carers ($r=.18$, $N=135$, $p<.05$) and those caring for a spouse rather than non-spouse (39 per cent compared with 19 per cent).[3] The relatively poorer health of spouse carers appeared to be attributable to age.

Other demographic differences in health were also age related. Older caregivers were less likely to report psychiatric-neurological disorders than younger caregivers ($r=-.21$, $N=135$, $p<.01$). Also, carers of those who were older were more likely to regard their health as good ($r=-.31$, $N=135$, $p<.001$). Both findings may reflect attrition from the caregiving population. Mention has already been made of the waiting lists for admission to nursing homes. Older caregivers and older carereceivers may have had greater access to alternative care, resulting in only the healthier caregivers continuing to care at home.

## *Is health related to burden and minor psychiatric symptoms?*

This question is best answered using the more global self-rated health measure. Self-rated health can be regarded as an index of poor physical well-being, a proposition which is supported by significant correlations with muscular-skeletal and heart-circulatory problems ($r=.18$, $N=136$, $p<.05$ and $r=.24$, $N=136$, $p<.01$ respectively) and a negligible correlation with reporting psychiatric-neurological disorders ($r=.01$, $N=136$, $p>.05$).

Contrary to expectations, perceptions of poor physical health were not related to burden. The correlation was a low and nonsignificant .10. In contrast, self-reported health was substantially related to the measures of anxiety and depression. The worse the perceived health of the caregiver, the higher the number of minor psychiatric symptoms reported ($r=.40$, $N=131$, $p<.001$).

Finding a relationship between physical and mental health is no surprise (Felton et al., 1984; Larson, 1978). Finding no relationship between burden and health deserves comment. These data indicate that a person in poor health is no more likely to believe that caregiving is threatening their basic needs than a person in good health. In other words, their physical health is not contaminating their reports of burden. This finding is both interesting and important. First, it reinforces the argument of burden being a subjective phenomenon. Second, since physical health is quite unrelated to burden, there is a need to consider health as a separate criterion from burden in evaluating caregiver well-being and home care feasibility.

The pattern of relationships suggests a further question which was not hypothesised but which deserves to be explored. Health may modify the burden–symptoms relationship such that those with good health have a better chance of preventing burden developing into symptoms than those without. Following Pedhazur (1982), a regression model was tested in which the interaction term (burden X health) was entered into the equation predicting symptoms after burden and health were entered separately. No significant variance was added by the interaction term, suggesting that the burden–symptom relationship did not vary with the health of the carer.

## Coping strategies

A list of the things that people might do to avoid being harmed by caregiving was compiled from the stress and caregiving literature and from talking to caregivers. Three kinds of coping responses were differentiated (Pearlin & Schooler, 1978). The first represented responses which changed the stressful situation. The second created more congenial perceptions of the situation. Pearlin and Schooler suggested two ways of changing the meaning of the situation — making positive comparisons (e.g. things could be worse) and selectively ignoring the problem and focusing on possible benefits (e.g. I'll be stronger for the experience). The third type of coping response altered neither the situation nor perceptions of the situation. The goal was not so much to avoid stress but to manage the stress reaction. Included in this category were cognitive strategies (e.g. acceptance is a virtue), emotional reactions (e.g. crying) or reliance on external factors (e.g. drugs, outings).

About one-third of the items used in the inventory were specific behaviours which were taken from Parker and Brown's (1982) instrument. They comprised problem solving, socialising, distraction, self-consolation and passivity. By focusing on behaviours, however, Parker and Brown did not represent emotional and cognitive strategies. Thus, additional items were developed. The final 28-item instrument was administered as a self-completion questionnaire, with caregivers being asked to indicate how frequently they used each strategy on a four-point scale ranging from never (1) to a lot (4).

The items were factor analysed using principal axes factor analyses followed by a varimax rotation. Four factors were extracted, accounting for 47 per cent of the variance. These factors served as a basis for developing four interrelated scales. The items comprising the scales appear in Table 9.2.

The first, called control, represented problem-focused strategies which were directed toward controlling the situation through seeking outside assistance and advice. The second scale represented emotion-focused coping and was called reinterpretation and acceptance. Cognitive strategies to change the meaning of the situation and to comfort oneself came together to define this scale. The reinterpretation items involved position comparisons (e.g. things could be worse) and selective ignoring (e.g. I'll be stronger for the experience). Other items reflected acceptance (e.g. having no alternative but to see things through) and efforts to manage stress symptoms (e.g. crying, having a cigarette).

Avoidance was the defining feature of the third scale which brought together items that involved actions to take one's mind off things. These activities (e.g. reading, busying yourself in work) were of a kind which could be implemented while in the caregiving role.

In contrast were the items of the fourth scale, which involved activities outside the caregiving situation. Going out with others and taking a break for a few days were strategies which distanced the

**Table 9.2    The items of the coping strategy scales and their frequency of use (N=138)**

| Coping strategy scales | % replying 'sometimes' or 'a lot' |
|---|---|
| **Control** | |
| Thinking through the problem | 81 |
| Discussing the problem with someone | 75 |
| Seeing the situation as a challenge to be met | 69 |
| Getting assistance with caring from relatives, friends or agencies | 65 |
| Using mechanical aids or devices to ease the caring load | 33 |
| **Reinterpretation and acceptance** | |
| Telling yourself there is no alternative and you just have to see it through | 82 |
| Telling yourself that there are others worse off than you | 77 |
| Telling yourself that things could be worse | 75 |
| Telling yourself it's the right thing to do | 70 |
| Telling yourself to take the good with the bad | 66 |
| Telling yourself it isn't as bad as all that | 63 |
| Telling yourself the problem can't last forever | 62 |
| Praying | 60 |
| Expressing your feelings (e.g. having a cry, letting off steam) | 59 |
| Thinking of the good things that have come out of the situation | 55 |
| Having a cigarette or a drink | 40 |
| Accepting hardship because it's meant to be | 40 |
| Telling yourself you will be a stronger and better person for the experience | 39 |
| **Avoidance** | |
| Busying yourself in work | 81 |
| Listening to music | 70 |
| Seeking warmth (e.g. sitting in front of a fire, in the sun, having a warm bath) | 60 |
| Reading a book | 53 |
| Taking tablets or medicines | 28 |
| **Withdrawal** | |
| Having a chat with close friends | 66 |
| Going out by yourself for a few hours | 50 |
| Going out with other people | 38 |
| Spending money on yourself | 30 |
| Taking a break for a few days or more | 22 |

carer from the caregiving situation. The scale, called withdrawal, involved physical separation, in contrast to avoidance, which ensured only cognitive separation. Withdrawal was more of a problem-focused coping strategy than avoidance. Although physical separation does not change the problem, it does provide the means for changing the individual. Withdrawal gives the opportunity for relaxation, rest and revitalisation to the caregiver.

All coping strategies were used, often in combination. Sixty-four per cent reported on average that they were using the control strategy sometimes or a lot. Applying the same cut-off to the other scales, 38 per cent used reinterpretation and acceptance, 35 per cent avoidance, and 10 per cent withdrawal. Basic statistical information on the scales is provided in Table 9.3.

**Table 9.3** **Alpha reliability coefficients (the diagonal), intercorrelations, means, and standard deviations for the coping strategy scales**

| Coping strategy scales | 1 | 2 | 3 | 4 |
|---|---|---|---|---|
| 1 Control | .65 | | | |
| 2 Reinterpretation and acceptance | .37 | .87 | | |
| 3 Avoidance | .27 | .49 | .70 | |
| 4 Withdrawal | .36 | .32 | .40 | .67 |
| *M* | 13.66 | 34.46 | 12.74 | 11.05 |
| *SD* | 3.09 | 8.53 | 3.45 | 2.83 |
| *N* | 132 | 134 | 132 | 133 |

## Demographic differences in coping strategies

Older caregivers were somewhat more likely to use avoidance strategies ($r=.16$, $N=130$, $p<.05$). Withdrawal strategies were used less often by spouse carers and older carers. In a stepwise multiple linear regression where age and spouse caring were used to predict withdrawal, carer's age was the only significant predictor ($\beta=-.20$, $p<.05$), accounting for 4 per cent of the variance in withdrawal ($F$ [1129] = 5.71, $p<.05$).

These findings raise the question of whether older carers stay home more because they want to or because they are less able to get out. Possibly, older caregivers are less interested in outings. Or they may simply have less energy for outings when they do get some time to themselves. On the other hand, older caregivers may have fewer opportunities because of little back-up support or because of lack of efficient transportation. The coping strategies that older carers use may not be so much a question of choice but necessity.

Reinterpretation and acceptance was a coping strategy favoured by female carers and carers with male recipients. In a stepwise multiple linear regression analysis, caregiver's gender was the only significant predictor ($\beta = .22$, $p<.05$), accounting for 5 per cent of the variance in the criterion ($F$ [1130] = 6.54, $p<.05$). If this coping strategy is related to burden, it may provide some insight into why women report greater burden in caregiving than men.

## Are coping strategies related to burden?

As seen in Table 9.4, coping strategies did not prevent perceptions of burden. Instead they appear to be a response to burden. The consistent pattern of positive correlations suggests that as burden increases, caregivers are prepared to try any strategy for dealing with the situation. Pearlin and Schooler's (1978) model of life strains, coping strategies and stress reactions seems to be a more appropriate one for dealing with these data. Burden represents one type of life strain or recognition of a threat. A person's coping strategies will come into play after the threat is recognised, determining whether or not a stress reaction is averted or induced by the threatening situation.

**Table 9.4   Correlations of the coping strategy scales with burden and minor psychiatric symptoms (N=129)[a]**

| Coping strategy scales | Burden | Minor psychiatric symptoms |
| --- | --- | --- |
| Control | .20** | −.06 |
| Withdrawal | .17* | −.06 |
| Reinterpretation and acceptance | .40*** | .37*** |
| Avoidance | .19* | .20** |

*Notes*:   a This is the minimum sample size on which any single correlation is based. The maximum is 133.
   *   $p<.05$          **   $p<.01$          ***   $p<.001$

## *Do coping strategies prevent minor psychiatric symptoms?*

To test this model, a hierarchical multiple linear regression analysis was carried out in which the coping strategies were entered into an equation predicting minor psychiatric symptoms after controlling for burden. In this way the frequency of use of coping strategies in response to threatening situations can be controlled and the effectiveness of the strategies ascertained from the beta weights. As can be seen from Table 9.5, the coping strategies behaved in a way which was consistent with the model, accounting for an additional 13 per cent of variance after controlling for burden ($F$ [4125] = 5.88, $p<.001$). The problem-focused strategies of control and withdrawal were associated with fewer minor psychiatric symptoms in caregivers. In contrast, reinterpretation and acceptance, the coping strategy used more frequently by women, was associated with more

**Table 9.5   Standardised linear regression coefficients and $R^2$ values for two models predicting minor psychiatric symptoms (N=129)**

| Predictor | Model 1 | Model 2 |
| --- | --- | --- |
| Burden | .43*** | .36*** |
| Withdrawal | | −.19* |
| Control | | −.22** |
| Avoidance | | .12 |
| Reinterpretation and acceptance | | .30** |
| $R^2$ | .19*** | .32*** |
| $R^2$ change | | .13*** |

*Notes*:   *   $p<.05$          **   $p<.01$          ***   $p<.001$

symptoms. The fourth coping strategy, avoidance, did not have a significant beta weight in the regression equation. This is not surprising given its high correlation with reinterpretation and acceptance ($r=.49$, $N=129$, $p<.001$).

Of particular interest in this analysis was the difference in effectiveness of withdrawal and avoidance. Withdrawal (involving physical separation from the caregiving role) appeared to be a useful coping strategy, whereas avoidance (switching off psychologically while remaining in the situation) proved to be of no benefit to the carer.

### Are personal resources a solution to burden?

No evidence emerged to support the notion that burden occurs when an 'unsuitable applicant' takes on the caregiving role. Contrary to expectations, carers were not at greater risk of experiencing burden if they were in poor health themselves, or if they were generally less energetic than most, or if they were not particularly interested in other people and their problems. Carers with very different personalities were represented at all levels of burden. The one exception arose with caregivers who reported feeling emotionally vulnerable and expressed little confidence in or respect for themselves. They were far more likely to report high burden. Interpreting these findings is difficult. One would expect that experiencing persistent burden would result in distress, low self-esteem and feelings of lack of control in the caregiver. One would be surprised if this did not occur given enough burden over a sufficiently long period of time. This does not preclude the possibility, however, of such responses being typical of the person before caregiving took place. Whether the emotional vulnerability or the burden came first is an issue which cannot be resolved from these data. Until a longitudinal study is undertaken to unravel these relationships, both possibilities should stand side by side as plausible explanations. Those who are easily aroused emotionally are vulnerable to burden, as they are to so many other stressors. At the same time, those who are experiencing burden have an increased likelihood of showing signs of emotional vulnerability.

While there appears to be little evidence of a personality profile of the 'burdened caregiver', there is reason to believe that some people respond to burden more effectively than others. The coping strategies which carers used influenced the degree to which they suffered from anxiety and depression. Problem-focused coping strategies were more effective than emotion-focused ones. Indeed, in this study, emotion-focused coping was associated with poor mental health among caregivers. Carers' stress reactions were less likely to be severe if they analysed the problem, sought advice, enlisted the help of others, and developed a plan of action. Also of benefit was distance from caregiving. Carers who treated themselves to occasional outings away from the caregiving situation fared better than carers who were equally burdened but unwilling or unable to leave.

These coping strategies were not used similarly by all demographic groups. First, women were more likely to use the ineffective coping strategy of reinterpretation and acceptance. In Chapter 11 we will look at how this affects women's greater experience of burden and symptoms. Second, the effective coping strategy of withdrawal was relatively unpopular among older caregivers. On the one hand, older carers may prefer to put their feet up and read the paper in the comfort of their own home. On the other hand, getting away from the caregiving situation may be under-utilised because older caregivers are unable to get out. Lack of transport may pose problems for some. Older caregivers are also predominantly spouse caregivers who are unlikely to have back-up support in the home to enable them to take a break. Furthermore, they are likely to feel greater reluctance and guilt about leaving their companion at home while they go out and enjoy themselves. Consideration should be given to making 'off site' breaks more available and acceptable to older caregivers, particularly those caring for a spouse.

# 10  Social and material resources

Theoretical tradition points to the importance of social integration and affiliation to well-being. Psychologists have regarded social relationships as satisfying inner needs or drives (Bowlby, 1973; Fromm, 1941; Maslow, 1954, 1962; Murray, 1938), whereas sociologists see the social environment as fundamental to the individual's sense of identity (Durkheim, 1951; Mead, 1934). We have seen in Chapter 2 that caregiving can seriously curtail the social activities of care providers. Carers are unable to go out, they have little time, energy or motivation for social interaction, and outsiders limit their visits for fear of choosing an inconvenient or awkward time to call. In such circumstances, the caregiver may be unable to sustain much social contact, and burden and poor mental health may follow. Theoretical tradition also sees social support as a buffer when individuals encounter problems (Cassel, 1976; Cobb, 1976; Dean & Lin, 1977). Social relationships provide individuals with moral support as well as aid in times of trouble (Croog, Lipson & Levine, 1972; Kahn & Antonucci, 1980). Burdened carers may turn to others to be told that they are doing well and have made the correct decisions, or they may seek assistance with chores and the sharing of responsibility. Such strategies may prevent loss of well-being. Both traditions are reflected in the present work. In Chapter 3, social support variables were envisaged as determinants of burden. Some were also considered as possible moderators or mediators, lessening the likelihood that burden would result in the emergence of minor psychiatric symptoms. Social support variables which mediated the burden-symptom relationship could be regarded as responses which carers might use to cope with their difficulties. Social support variables which moderated the burden-symptom relationship were attributes which did not come about through burden but which could prove advantageous, buffering burdened carers.

Two definitions of social support are particularly relevant to the way in which the term 'social resources' is used here: Social support as the information that one is esteemed and loved and belongs to a socially cohesive community (Cobb, 1976), and social support as interpersonal transaction involving concern, aid and information about oneself and the environment (House, 1981). Incorporating both these ideas, social resources were defined in terms of interacting with others, receiving assistance from others, and knowing that others could be called upon should assistance be required.

### Interacting with others

Both the quantity and quality of caregivers' social relationships were assessed but the question of adequacy was avoided completely. The decision to concentrate on 'how much?' and 'what type?' at the expense of 'is it enough?' was made because adequacy measures risked being confounded with the dependant variable, burden. It will be recalled that perceived threat to one's sense of belonging, a notion very similar to adequacy, was defined as part of the burden construct.

Three measures of social interaction were used: the extent to which social interaction was available, the extent to which it had changed as a result of caregiving, and the extent to which the carer had a confidant. The Availability of Social Interaction Scale ($\alpha$ = .71) comprised six items from the Interview Schedule for Social Interaction (ISSI) (Henderson et al., 1981): 1) how many people they had contact with in an ordinary week, 2) how many people they shared common interests with, 3) how many people they could ask favours of, 4) how many friends they had who could visit at any time regardless of circumstances, 5) how many friends and relatives they had who they could talk with freely and frankly, and 6) how many people there were who depended on them particularly for help or advice. The scoring system followed that adopted in the ISSI, with seven being the maximum number of people coded for any individual item. Scores were normally distributed ranging from 1 to 42 with a mean of 26.22 ($SD$ = 9.26).

Change in social interaction was assessed by asking carers to compare their social interactions now with those preceding caregiving. Responses of more (1), the same (2), or less (3) were coded for the first five items taken from the Availability of Social Interaction Scale and summed to produce the Social Interaction Loss Scale ($\alpha$ = .73). Scores ranged from 5 to 15 with a mean of 11.09 ($SD$ = 1.87). Forty per cent of the sample averaged a no-change score, 51 per cent averaged a score between no-change and loss, and only 9 per cent averaged a score between no-change and an increase.

A dominant theme in the social support literature is the importance of close, intimate relationships as opposed to casual relationships (Brown & Harris, 1978; Lowenthal & Haven, 1968), the former being regarded as crucial to well-being. Consequently, a scale was devised which focused specifically on close relationships.

The Availability of a Confidant Scale ($\alpha$ = .57) comprised five items which again were taken from the Interview Schedule for Social Interaction (Henderson et al., 1981). Caregivers replied no (1) or yes (2) to the following: Is there a particular person who 1) you feel you can lean on, 2) you feel very close to, 3) shares your happiness with you, 4) shares your most private feelings, and 5) gives you a hug? The vast majority of carers were well catered for in terms of these criteria. Scores ranged from five to ten but the mean was a high 9.23 ($SD$ = 1.11).

*Demographic differences on social interaction*

Most variation between demographic groups occurred on the Availability of Social Interaction Scale. Scores were substantially higher among younger, non-spouse carers and those with older dependants. In a stepwise multiple linear regression analysis, caring for someone other than a spouse emerged as the single significant predictor ($\beta$ = 0.34, $p<.001$), accounting for 12 per cent of the variance ($F$ [1134] = 17.80, $p<.001$).

This finding supports the concern that has been expressed about the isolation of spouse caregivers (Fengler & Goodrich, 1979; Gilleard, 1984b). The person they are caring for is not merely a dependant but more than likely their lifelong companion — a person with whom they have always spent most of their spare time. Spouses are likely to play a central role in the carer's social network. Consequently, as the carereceiver's capacity to maintain social ties is reduced, so too is the caregiver's and the two become increasingly isolated from others.

Other demographic differences involved minimal loss of social interaction among carers with older dependants ($r=-.18$, $N=137$, $p<.05$) and the greater availability of a confidant for female carers ($M=9.41$, $SD=.93$) than male carers ($M=8.71$, $SD=1.40$).[1] The latter finding mirrors a consistent trend in the social support literature toward women reporting more intimate relationships than men (Henderson et al., 1981). The former result is similar to a number reported earlier in which favourable caregiving circumstances have been linked with older carereceivers. Again a survivor effect is considered the most plausible explanation. Those who remain in the community at an older age must do so in optimal caring circumstances. Otherwise their advanced age and their longer period of eligibility (e.g. on waiting lists for longer) would facilitate their admission to a hostel or nursing home.

*Is social interaction related to burden and mental health?*

Burden was not related to any of the social interaction variables, but symptoms were more likely to occur when the caregiver had low levels of social interaction and reported being engaged in less social activity than was the case prior to caregiving (see Table 10.1).

**Table 10.1    Correlations of the social interaction scales with burden and minor psychiatric symptoms (N=133)[a]**

| Social interaction scales | Burden | Minor psychiatric symptoms |
|---|---|---|
| Availability of a confidant | .03 | −.03 |
| Availability of social interaction | .10 | −.21** |
| Loss of availability of social interaction | −.06 | .21** |

*Notes*:    a This is the minimum sample size on which any single correlation is based. The maximum is 134.

\*    $p<.05$        \*\*    $p<.01$        \*\*\*    $p<.001$

Although neither a mediating nor moderating hypothesis has been proposed in relation to these particular variables in Chapter 3, the pattern of intercorrelations invited further investigation. In theory, one could argue that burden results in less social interaction and this, in turn, will lead to the development of symptoms. The data, however, did not support this interpretation. An alternative way of thinking about social interaction was that it was unrelated to burden but would protect those with good social networks from the adverse consequences of burden, namely, anxiety and depression. Although some support for this interpretation could be found, the evidence was not strong. In a hierarchical regression analysis, the interaction term of burden and the availability of social interaction added a significant 5 per cent of variance to that accounted for by these variables separately ($F [1126]=8.46$, $p<.01$). Yet Figure 10.1 shows how slight the difference was in the relationships between burden and symptoms when social interaction was high and when it was low.

**Figure 10.1    The relationship between burden and minor psychiatric symptoms in carers when their social interaction is high and low**

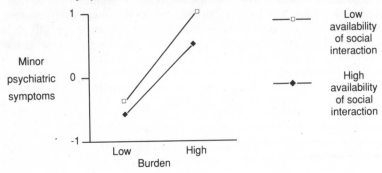

## Receiving assistance from others

As mentioned earlier, assistance may take the form of moral support, which seeks to improve the carer's mood or feelings of well-being, or instrumental support, which is oriented toward helping the carer's overt performance directly. The assistance may come from informal sources (those who do not have as their primary function the provision of support) or formal sources (professionals whose primary function is to give help (Veiel, 1985). These dimensions were used to define three assistance variables — informal moral support, informal instrumental support and formal support.

Three measures of informal support were used. Caregivers were asked first, if family and later, if friends: 1) admired what they were doing, 2) thought they had taken on too much, and 3) took their contribution for granted (reverse scored). Scores ranged from 3 (no support) to 9 (full support) for both the Family Support Scale ($\alpha$ = .65) and the Friends' Support Scale ($\alpha$ = .52). The mean for the Family Support Scale was 6.67 ($SD$ = 2.11) and for the Friends' Support Scale 7.13 ($SD$ = 1.69).

The third moral support measure was a Family Closeness Scale ($\alpha$ = .77) in which carers were asked whether or not the care-receiver's family 1) kept in touch, 2) kept their problems to themselves (reverse scored), 3) expressed concern about each other, and 4) were close. Scores ranged from 4 to 8 but the distribution was very skewed with a mean of 7.06 ($SD$ = 1.28).

Instrumental support from family, friends and neighbours was measured through two scales representing assistance with caregiving and help with household chores. Assistance with caregiving was indexed by adding responses to the items: 1) have you asked for help and received it, and 2) have you been offered help and accepted it. The intercorrelation for the two items was .35. Scores ranged from 2 to 4 with a mean of 3.06 ($SD$ = .82). Of interest was the finding that just less than one-third of caregivers (30 per cent) scored 2, meaning that they received no informal instrumental support at all. Moreover, lack of use of such support could not be attributed to the fact that the carereceiver was only mildly impaired. Use of informal instrumental support bore no relationship to the workload variables.

Assistance with daily activities was assessed by whether or not anyone other than the carer was regularly involved in the household chores of: 1) shopping, 2) major meal preparation, 3) minor meal preparation, 4) light cleaning, 5) heavy cleaning, 6) laundry, 7) ironing, 8) minor house repairs, 9) gardening, 10) handling finances, and 11) transport. Scores on the Assistance with Daily Living Scale ($\alpha$ = .74) ranged from 11 to 21 and were highly skewed with most caregivers receiving relatively little assistance. The mean was 13.48 ($SD$ = 2.34).

Finally, the formal services which were available to carereceivers and caregivers could be classified into three general categories. Household task relief was provided by the government-funded services, Meals on Wheels and Home Help, to 17 per cent and 27 per cent respectively. Relief from caregiving was provided to 14 per cent by Care at Home (a private home support agency), to 58 per cent by Day Care Centres and to 30 per cent through Shared Care (respite care). Support with caregiving, as opposed to relief from caregiving, was obtained through three organisations. The Mobile Rehabilitation Unit provided equipment and aids, installed bathroom rails and ramps, and advised on and organised house modifications in 52 per cent of cases. Community nurses assisted 88 per cent by bathing and administering medication to the carereceiver, and often by giving moral support and advice to the caregiver. The third source of formal assistance was offered by the Carers' Support Group, a self-help community group which aimed to provide information and moral support to its members and which was used by 8 per cent of carers. The use of formal support was scored for each service separately and for the number of services used.

*Demographic differences in assistance received*

Gender and spouse-caring differences dominated the demographic breakdown of the assistance variables. Women who were caring received more moral support from family ($M$=6.98, $SD$=1.96) than did men who were caring ($M$=5.77, $SD$=2.29).[2] Support from friends was also greater among female carers as well as among younger carers. Caregivers' gender proved to be the only significant predictor ($\beta$ = .21, $p$<.05) in a stepwise regression analysis which accounted for 4 per cent of the variance ($F$ [1129] = 6.02, $p$<.05).

A second gender difference in assistance received involved the Meals on Wheels service. Male caregivers were more likely to benefit from Meals on Wheels (31 per cent) than female caregivers (12 per cent).[3] In part this may reflect men's attitude to the traditionally female task of cooking. Unfortunately, it is also consistent with a bias observed in how the service was administered. Female caregivers complained of being refused assistance for their co-resident elderly parents on the grounds that women were more able to prepare meals than men. Exceptions did not appear to be made in the case of women who were working. In the words of one daughter, 'I dash home from work in my lunch hour to organise Mum's lunch. I tried leaving her a salad or soup in a thermos but she just won't bother when she's alone. I need to be there to sit her down with it'. This task could have been performed by Meals on

Wheels. Hopefully, this form of discrimination against female carers will have been rectified by the time this book is published. The broader concern that community services are geared more to the needs of men than women should not be dismissed lightly. Abel (1987) has referred to this inequity in formal service delivery in the United States and Gibson and Allen (1988) have argued that such discrimination is entrenched in the way in which community services have been developed in Australia.

The third gender difference involved the use of the respite care programme, Shared Care. In contrast to the above findings, more women made use of this programme (38 per cent) than men (8 per cent).[4] Since women also reported higher burden scores in this study than men, greater use of respite care may have been reflecting greater need. This was not the case. When burden was controlled, the gender–respite care relationship remained significant.

Turning now to differences between spouse and non-spouse carers, the assistance provided varied in three areas. First, greater family closeness characterised spouse carers ($M=7.43$, $SD=.92$) than non-spouse carers ($M=6.77$, $SD=1.45$).[5] This difference is consistent with reports of family tensions when parent care is required (Cath, 1972; Rogers, 1981). Siblings may differ in their views about the sort of care needed, past rivalries may re-emerge, and resentment may occur when family members fail to rally to the cause. In one case, a family had moved interstate with their elderly relative on two occasions within a short period of time. The carer's sisters had not offered assistance: 'You keep going', they had said, 'she's happiest with you'. Later in the interview it transpired that the sisters resented the fact that the carer had moved their mother away from them some years before. These problems are less likely to arise when a spouse is available and assumes the caregiving role.

Help with household tasks was greater for those caring for someone other than a spouse, for younger caregivers, and for carers of older dependants. In a stepwise multiple linear regression analysis, non-spouse caregiving emerged as the only significant predictor ($\beta = -.30$, $p<.001$), accounting for 9 per cent of the variance ($F$ [1134] $= 13.01$, $p<.001$). Non-spouse caregivers were usually caring for parents and had their own spouses and sometimes children in the same house to help with daily chores. In contrast, those caring for their spouses were unlikely to have anyone else living at home.

Spouse carers were compensated to some extent by the finding that they were the major beneficiaries of Home Help (42 per cent compared with 15 per cent of nonspouse carers).[6] This service was also more likely to assist older caregivers ($r=.28$, $N=137$, $p<.001$). Home Help was provided to elderly men or women with medical certification that they were unable to perform household cleaning tasks for themselves.

The remaining demographic differences were age related. Younger carers relied on Day Centre more, probably because their work commitments led to the need for such support during working hours ($r=-.16$, $N=137$, $p<.05$). Older carers more frequently used the Mobile Rehabilitation Unit ($r=.15$, $N=137$, $p<.05$). Again, need was considered the most likely explanation. With failing strength and agility themselves, older carers need advice and assistance to avoid physical strain, injury and psychological distress for either partner. Finally, what has been referred to previously as the survivor effect was evident once more, with carers of older care-receivers obtaining more informal instrumental assistance ($r=.18$, $N=137$, $p<.05$).

## Does assistance from others relieve burden and improve mental health?

Of the 14 assistance measures, only four were significantly related to burden or mental well-being and three of these were in the opposite direction to that predicted. Contrary to expectations, moral support from family or friends was not associated with lower burden and fewer minor psychiatric symptoms, but with greater burden and more symptoms (see Table 10.2). This suggests that moral support may be a response to signals for help. If social support is forthcoming when carers show signs of burden, moral support, like coping strategies, may halt the progression of the carer from a state of burden to states of anxiety and depression. To examine this proposition, a hierarchical stepwise regression analysis was carried out. Scales measuring support from family and friends were entered into the equation predicting psychiatric symptoms after controlling for the degree of burden they were experiencing. No evidence emerged, however, to support the effectiveness of moral support in reducing the likelihood of minor psychiatric illness. Indeed, once burden was controlled, moral support appeared to be unrelated to mental health.

Before leaving the subject of moral support, the absence of any significant negative association between the closeness of the family and the burden and stress experienced by the caregiver is worthy of mention. One might have expected caregiving to be less burdensome when the family was close and more likely to share the responsibility. For instance, Zarit et al.'s (1980) data suggest that families may be effective in reducing caregiving burden by visiting the carereceiver regularly. The present data indicate that family cohesiveness neither systematically exacerbates nor alleviates the burden of home care. In view of this unexpected finding, a hier-

**Table 10.2** Correlations of assistance provided with burden and minor psychiatric symptoms (*N*=131)[a]

| Assistance provided | Burden | Minor psychiatric symptoms |
| --- | --- | --- |
| Moral support | | |
|   Family support | .26*** | .15* |
|   Friends' support | .30*** | .23** |
|   Family closeness | .02 | −.09 |
| Informal instrumental support | | |
|   Assistance with caregiving | −.08 | −.04 |
|   Assistance with daily activities | −.07 | .06 |
| Formal support | | |
|   Meals on Wheels | −.12 | −.13 |
|   Home Help | .09 | .06 |
|   Care at Home | −.05 | −.17 |
|   Shared Care | .29*** | .20** |
|   Day Care | .06 | −.07 |
|   Mobile Rehabilitation Unit | .06 | −.01 |
|   Community Nurses | −.08 | −.03 |
|   Carers' Support Group | −.01 | −.20** |
|   No. of support services used | .11 | −.06 |

*Notes:*  a  This is the minimum sample size on which any single correlation is based. The maximum is 134.
    *   $p<.05$     **   $p<.01$     ***   $p<.001$

archical regression analysis was carried out to explore the possibility of family closeness playing a buffering role. The interaction term added a significant 7 per cent of variance ($F$ [1123]=11.94, $p<.001$) to that accounted for by the individual variables. Figure 10.2 shows that the increase in symptoms accompanying increased burden is less when family ties are very strong. These data suggest that while family closeness cannot prevent burden, those with close families are better equipped to withstand the development of symptoms when they become burdened.

**Figure 10.2** The relationship between burden and minor psychiatric symptoms in carers when the family is very close and less close

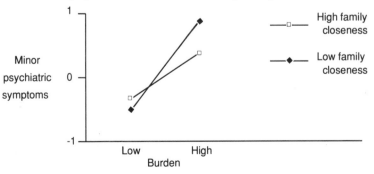

Turning to informal instrumental support, deeds were no more effective than words in reducing burden or stress and formal support faired little better (see Table 10.2). Furthermore, there was little evidence that these variables mediated or moderated the burden–symptoms relationship. Yet, those who participated in the Carers' Support Group were less likely to report feelings of anxiety or depression. It is of note that users of this service saw themselves as being neither more nor less burdened than non-users. Possibly these results reflect a selection bias. Those who are depressed and anxious, regardless of whether they are giving care, may feel more apathetic and less inclined to see any value in attending self-help groups.

The only other significant relationship between formal service use and caregiving burden and stress involved the respite service, Shared Care. Those who made use of respite care were higher on burden and higher in reporting minor psychiatric symptoms. These findings almost certainly reflect a selection effect. Shared Care was not a service that was widely available. Only those high in need were likely to be considered and were prepared to suffer the inflexibility in the way the service was administered. Bookings for Shared Care had to be made well in advance, they could not be changed readily, and the placements were sometimes not to the liking of either the caregiver or carereceiver. Shared Care was used by carers more as an answer to desperation than as a means of prevention.

The absence of notable relationships between formal service use and outcome measures was disappointing, but is consistent with a considerable body of other research in this area (Ballinger, 1984; Gilleard et al., 1984a; Greene & Timbury, 1979; Pratt et al., 1985; Wells & Jorm, 1987; Zarit et al., 1980). The first question one might ask is whether caregivers were satisfied with the help they were receiving. The overwhelming majority were (Braithwaite, 1986b). Furthermore, the dissatisfied minority did not distinguish themselves from others by their greater burden or poorer mental health. Satisfaction with services was no better a predictor of burden and mental distress than usage of services.

However, to conclude that services have failed to reduce burden and stress in the caregiver is unjustified. Again, selection effects may, and indeed should be operating in most of these situations. If over-servicing of government-sponsored support is being avoided, services should be directed only to those in need. Those in need hopefully include the majority of high burden caregivers. To reduce their stress below that of low need non-service users would be overly ambitious. Therefore, one cannot realistically expect to find positive correlations between service use and well-being. Any fair evaluation must control for need prior to service use.

**Knowing that others could be called upon**

Knowing that support was available was the third and final aspect of the social resources domain which was examined. Three measures were used. The first was concerned with backup. Carers were asked whether or not they had family or friends who would take over if they were out of action for: 1) 2 or 3 days, and 2) 2 or 3 weeks. The two items correlated .34. Scores ranged from 2 to 4, with a substantial 23 per cent obtaining 2, meaning that they had no friends or family to provide backup support even for 2 or 3 days. The mean was 3.10 ($SD$ = .74).

The second awareness measure focused not only on whether anyone was available to help, but also on the caregiver's willingness to ask. In other words, the value of social support to the carer was assessed, rather than simply the presence of support. If help was not sought because either the carer or the carereceiver refused to have anyone else involved, the support network could be irrelevant.

Caregivers indicated how willing they were to ask relatives or friends for help in the future. Responses were made on a three-point rating scale: 1) no, under no circumstances, 2) only if absolutely necessary, and 3) yes, willingly. Nineteen per cent replied no and 31 per cent said that they would seek help only in special circumstances. The remaining 50 per cent expressed unequivocal willingness to ask for assistance.

The third scale was more subjective than the other two and assessed the amount of support carers felt they had in caring. The Sole Responsibility Scale ($\alpha$ = .55) comprised three items ascertaining whether carers: 1) felt they had total responsibility for the well-being of another person, 2) feared what would happen if they were unable to provide care, and 3) wondered if the person they were caring for was all right when they were not with them. The scores on the Sole Responsibility Scale ranged from 3 to 6 and were highly skewed, the mean being 5.61 ($SD$ = .73). This suggests that being a caregiver is a lonely role.

Differences between groups were most marked on awareness of backup support. Greater backup was reported by younger, non-spouse carers and carers with older dependants. In a stepwise multiple linear regression analysis, non-spouse caring emerged as the major and sole predictor ($\beta$ = $-$.30, $p$<.001), accounting for 9 per cent of the variance in the criterion ($F$ [1133] = 13.21, $p$<.001). The only other demographic difference was a greater willingness on the part of caregivers with older dependants to ask for help ($r$=.18, $N$=135, $p$<.05). Again this is consistent with the picture that is being built up of a special caregiving relationship for older dependants.

*Is awareness of support related to burden and mental health?*

Neither backup support nor willingness to ask for help were related to reports of burden or minor psychiatric symptoms (see Table 10.3) nor did they buffer burdened carers from the development of symptoms. Although the burden–backup interaction term contributed an additional 13 per cent to the variance accounted for in symptoms ($F$ [1125] = 23.69, $p<.001$) in a hierarchical regression analysis, backup benefited low-burdened carers rather than high-burdened carers (see Figure 10.3).

**Figure 10.3    The relationship between burden and minor psychiatric symptoms in carers with high backup support and low backup support**

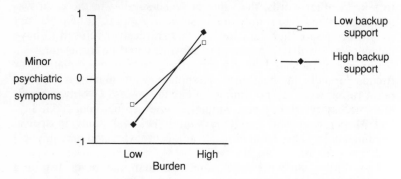

The third awareness of support variable, feeling solely responsible for caregiving, was significantly related to both burden and symptoms. High burden and poor mental health were more likely to occur among carers who believed themselves to be solely responsible for the carereceiver's well-being.

**Table 10.3    Correlations of the awareness of support measures with burden and minor psychiatric symptoms ($N$=132)[a]**

| Awareness of support measures | Burden | Minor psychiatric symptoms |
|---|---|---|
| Backup support | −.03 | .00 |
| Willingness to use informal support | −.09 | −.11 |
| Sole responsibility | .43*** | .20** |

Notes:  a This is the minimum sample size on which any single correlation is based. The maximum is 135.
        ** $p<.01$          *** $p<.001$

**Conclusion: Are social resources useful?**

Being unwilling or unable to share responsibility for care appears to be an attitude not so much of the 'super-carer' as of the carer at risk. Feeling solely responsible was indicative of both high burden and poor mental health. Less certainty surrounds the issue of directionality. Being unable to share the responsibility may mean that carers are overloaded from the outset and therefore prime targets for stress. Alternatively, the carer who feels she is showing signs of not coping may become almost obsessive about proving she can cope, and in so doing, disregard offers of help from others. Here the attitude of sole responsibility is a consequence rather than a cause of stress. Whatever the direction, the evidence is clear that bearing sole responsibility is a danger signal in terms of the well-being of the caregiver.

Although the core measures of social support failed to predict burden, some evidence did emerge to support the buffering hypothesis. Two aspects of social support — the closeness of one's family, and to a lesser extent, the size of one's social network — appeared to advantage burdened carers because the likelihood of symptoms developing in such cases was reduced. This finding did not extend, however, to the variables which directly addressed the 'helping' function of friends and relatives. There was no evidence that a network of friends and family saying or doing supportive things protected carers from the risk of poor mental health.

The absence of any link between informal assistance and well-being goes against conventional wisdom, but is not peculiar to this research. Zarit et al. (1980, 1986) failed to find significant relationships between the amount of support carers received and their feelings of burden. Fiore et al. (1983) reported that even the helpfulness of the support was unrelated to depression. What was important was the degree of upset carers experienced in their social relationships. Consistent with the importance of upset is the well-documented importance of carers' perceptions of need for more support. In this study, the need for more support was not measured because it was not conceptually distinct from the love and belongingness component of the burden construct. Other studies, however, have tried to differentiate the two and have concluded that carers who are under stress are more likely to see their social support as inadequate (George & Gywther, 1986; Zarit et al., 1986). If the correct interpretation is that perceived lack of support contributes to stress, these studies and others suggest that the crucial warning sign is not the defective level of support, but a subjectively perceived deficit in it.

A second interpretation, and one which cannot be discounted, is that when stressed, we are more likely to perceive deficits in our support network, regardless of the level of assistance being received. This line of argument gives rise to the notion that no amount of help is enough for carers who feel burdened, depressed or anxious.

Such a position, however, denies social support the special status it deserves. If burden is primarily a function of other factors such as degeneration, unpredictability and lack of choice, providing assistance is unlikely to have a marked impact on burden. The presence or absence of such support is likely to pale into insignificance alongside something like the deterioration of a much loved family member. This is not to say, however, that caregivers who are experiencing burden or distress do not appreciate or take comfort in the help that others offer. An analogous situation is dealing with the death of a spouse or parent. The assistance offered by others does not and cannot reduce the pain, but rarely is that support forgotten by the bereaved. Indeed, on balance, the findings in this chapter appeared to be saying that social support does serve at least one important function. Being there for someone who is burdened is more important than doing anything in particular. Through being there, friends and relatives may help the carer withstand further loss of mental well-being. This finding has important implications for those friends and relatives who withdraw from caregiving situations saying, 'There's no point in going over. There's nothing I can do.'

Inconclusive findings surround the issue of formal support. Greater carer well-being was not associated with the use of or satisfaction with services offered to carereceivers. The finding was disappointing but not surprising. For a positive result to occur, the stress experienced by those using and needing services would have to be reduced below that of those not using and not needing services. No service provider would argue that this is a reasonable goal. The value of services is to be measured more often in terms of turning unbearable problems into bearable ones, than in terms of making problems disappear altogether. Therefore, before any conclusions can be reached on service effectiveness, evaluation studies must be undertaken which, first, control for the needs of the caregiver and carereceiver, and, second, employ outcome measures which are sufficiently sensitive to detect possible benefits to users. This study was not designed to meet either of these criteria.

**Material resources**

The carer's perceptions of financial adequacy along with measures of the occupational status of caregiver and carereceiver constituted material resources. Occupational status was defined in terms of the major breadwinner's longstanding occupation before retirement. There were three categories: High — professional, managerial (1), Middle — sales, clerical, skilled (2), and Low — semi-skilled, unskilled (3). Only 17 per cent of caregiving families and only 25 per cent of carereceivers or the spouses of carereceivers fell into the lower occupational group.

Financial adequacy was assessed by asking caregivers if there was enough money to meet the carereceiver's needs. The vast majority considered there to be sufficient funds (87 per cent), 4 per cent described the situation as borderline, and 9 per cent reported needing more.

Groups differed on these variables in three ways. First, caregivers who lived separately from carereceivers were more likely to belong to the high occupational group (63 per cent) than those who were cohabitating (34 per cent).[7] Undoubtedly the salaries of professional and managerial breadwinners make possible house extensions, granny flats or the purchase of a house next door. Second, carers' perceptions of financial adequacy were greater when care was being provided to an older person ($r=.23$, $N=143$, $p<.05$), another finding consistent with the survivor effect. The third demographic difference was surprising and cannot be readily explained. Female carereceivers (37 per cent) were more likely to come from high socio-economic families than male carereceivers (20 per cent).[8] Such a finding should not be regarded as indicative of the economic well-being of elderly women. Poverty has been shown to be a major problem for this group (Abel, 1987; Crystal, 1982; Rosenman, 1982).

When the material resources variables were correlated with burden and minor psychiatric symptoms, two significant relationships emerged (see Table 10.4). Symptoms were more prevalent among the lower occupational groups regardless of whether the occupational classification was that of the caregiving family or of the carereceiver. The findings are consistent with epidemiological work which has shown a greater prevalence of neurosis in lower socio-economic groups (Kessler & Cleary, 1980; Schwab & Schwab, 1978). Contrary to predictions, burden was not significantly related to either occupational status or financial adequacy.

**Table 10.4  Correlations of the material well-being indices with burden and minor psychiatric symptoms ($N=133$)[a]**

| Material well-being indices | Burden | Minor psychiatric symptoms |
|---|---|---|
| Occupational status | | |
| Caregiver | .10 | .24** |
| Carereceiver | −.01 | .20** |
| Financial adequacy | −.05 | .04 |

*Notes:*  a  This is the minimum sample size on which any single correlation is based. The maximum is 135.
　　　** $p<.01$

In Chapter 3, it was suggested that material resources may moderate the burden-symptom relationship, protecting the affluent and leaving the poor vulnerable. To test this, regression models were set up in which burden, a material resource variable and the interaction between burden and the material resource variable were used to predict symptoms. Only in the case of the carereceiver's socio-economic status did the interaction term add a significant proportion of variance (10 per cent) ($F$ [1126] = 19.51, $p<.001$). Figure 10.4 shows that carers whose recipient came from a high socio-economic family did not have the same increase in symptoms as carers whose recipient came from a low socio-economic family.

**Figure 10.4    The relationship between burden and minor psychiatric symptoms in carers of high SES recipients and medium-low SES recipients**

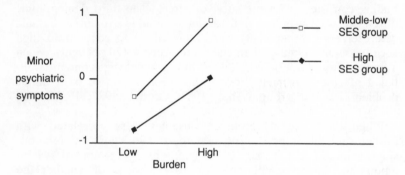

Before concluding this chapter, a note of caution is warranted in drawing inferences from the analyses of the material resource variables. Such findings have important implications for home care policies oriented to reducing burden. To draw such inferences from these data, however, is premature. The middle-class bias in this sample has already been noted. The financial adequacy measure adds weight to this observation by demonstrating just how affluent this sample was. Only 13 per cent were concerned about their financial situation in relation to caregiving. Further data are needed from a less affluent sample before we can be confident about the role which material resources play in relation to caregiving burden. All we can say at this point is that the caregivers of the more privileged look as if they may be just as burdened but better able to avoid symptoms than carers of the less privileged.

# 11 Predicting and understanding burden: A synthesis

The factors contributing to caregiving burden have now been examined in some detail—workload, the crises of decline, personal resources, social resources, and material resources. The caregiving cake has been dissected and the slices examined individually, but at no point have they been put together to find out which are the more important and whether the objective variables contribute more to our understanding of burden than the subjective.

## Toward a synthesis: Factors not predicting burden

Before examining what did predict burden and mental ill health, the factors which were not relevant in the present study will be reviewed briefly.

First, the workload variables, which sought to incorporate both the instrumental and social-emotional responsibilities of the caregiver, contributed little to our understanding of burden and symptoms. The only indication of workload having some impact was in the area of supervision. The greater the tendency to supervise, the more likely the presence of minor psychiatric symptoms. With this exception, the responsibilities of caregiving were quite unrelated to the carer's reactions to caregiving.

Informal help was considerably less important than assumed. Neither instrumental nor emotional support from others affected the burden carers experienced or the symptoms they reported. The risks to well-being experienced by carers were reduced, however, by some aspects of social resources—having others to interact with and to share responsibility with. Neither were competing commitments—the extent to which carers had additional responsibilities to children, spouses or employers—correlates of burden and symptoms, though the subjective measure, time constraints, was. Fourth, the personality inventories failed to provide convincing support for the notion that some people are personally suited to caring while others are not. Carers who perceived little threat or reported few symptoms were no more likely to be sociable, kind or active than those who showed high burden or many symptoms. The

117

notion that some people are more vulnerable when faced with stressful experiences, however, remains a plausible hypothesis. Further testing of this proposition with a prospective rather than cross-sectional research design is necessary to disentangle the traits of emotionality, self-esteem and mastery from the states of anxiety and depression.

Finally, we failed to find support for the effectiveness of formal support services. As with the emotional vulnerability hypothesis, the design of the study made these findings inconclusive rather than disconfirmatory. Since the needs of the carereceivers in the study varied enormously, proper controls could not be introduced for this variable. It would be overly optimistic to expect to adequately examine service effectiveness without designing the study at the outset to control for a host of possible confounding variables. All we can note from the data available are overwhelming reports of satisfaction with the services which were used (Braithwaite, 1986b).

## Toward a synthesis: The predictors of burden

As a first step in examining the relative importance of the significant predictors of burden, a stepwise multiple linear regression analysis was carried out. The variables which were entered into this analysis as predictors had statistically significant correlations with the criterion and were the best of their type in that they accounted for significant proportions of variance in earlier regression analyses. The predictors were the number of confidants of the carereceiver (Chapter 7), the sole responsibility index (Chapter 10), the emotional and cognitive impairment scales (Chapter 8)[1], learning about caregiving (Chapter 8), the time constraints scale (Chapter 8), the autonomy scale (Chapter 8), having a breaking point (Chapter 8), preferred nursing home admission (Chapter 8), symp-

Table 11.1    Correlations and beta weights for the regression of burden on the major explanatory variables (N=118)

| Major explanatory variables | r | Beta |
|---|---|---|
| No. of carereceiver's confidants | .21** | ns |
| Sole responsibility | .43*** | .28*** |
| Emotional and cognitive impairment | .55*** | .29*** |
| Learning about caregiving | .31*** | .13* |
| Time constraints | .52*** | .32*** |
| Autonomy | −.23** | ns |
| Breaking point* | .27*** | .19** |
| Preferred nursing home admission | .24** | ns |
| Minor psychiatric symptoms | .43*** | .18** |
| Caregiver's gender | .19* | ns |

*Notes:*    *  $p<.05$        **  $p<.01$        ***  $p<.001$

toms of minor psychiatric illness (Chapter 9)[2], and gender (Chapter 6). Together these variables accounted for a substantial 62 per cent of variance in caregiving burden (see Table 11.1).

*The variables which became superfluous*

Four variables which correlated significantly with burden individually did not have significant beta weights in the final regression analysis — the carereceiver's confidants, autonomy, preferred nursing home admission, and gender. Correlations among predictors, further regression analyses and changing beta weights explained why these variables no longer contributed to the regression equation.

Carereceivers who had many confidants were more likely to have carers who reported severe time constraints. In the final regression analysis, time constraints proved to be the major predictor. These findings conflict with the interpretation made in Chapter 7 that having many confidants was a source of tension in the caregiver–carereceiver relationship. It seems that the alternative notion of carereceivers looking elsewhere for confidants through necessity was closer to the mark. Burdened carers were busy carers whose care recipients found others to talk to.

The autonomy variable reflected the degree to which the recipient of care had allowed the provider of care independence in the past. Autonomy failed to emerge as a significant predictor because of overlap with emotional disturbance. Carers who reported emotionally disruptive behaviour in the carereceiver were more likely to perceive themselves as being dominated by the carereceiver in the past. The finding can be interpreted as support for the view that those who are difficult to care for in old age were probably difficult at a younger age as well (Costa & McCrae, 1983; Neugarten, 1965; Robinson & Thurnher, 1979).

At the same time it would be unwise to assume that constancy over time means constancy across relationships. Difficult behaviour may typify a particular caregiving relationship. Carers often expressed anger and distress at how troublesome the person they were caring for could be at home alone with them, but how pleasant and cooperative they were in the presence of others, particularly doctors, nurses, social workers, and the like. One carer described how her husband would refuse to use his walking frame properly, would overbalance and fall, pulling her over with him. When the physiotherapist visited the home, however, he walked steadily with the frame, 'behaving beautifully'. Such accounts were not unusual, and carers recalled their frustration, sometimes embarrassment, because they could not get others to understand their difficulties. On the other side of the coin are the sometimes naive judgements of professionals. They can be quick to recall carers who did not impress them by complaining incessantly about care recipients who they 'knew' to be cooperative and delightful clients.

The practice of categorising people as this way or that is dangerous because it forces us into a situation of deciding whose assessment is right and whose is wrong. A far more useful model is to view human behaviour as changing with the social situation. Disruptive behaviour is not necessarily a fixed characteristic of a person nor is it caused by a carer. Rather it is a characteristic way in which a person behaves toward someone else in a particular context. Just as a caregiving relationship may bring out the best in one or both partners, it may bring out the worst.

The third variable which disappeared in the multiple linear regression analysis was preference for a nursing home placement. The common variance between this variable and burden was explained by the carer's level of minor psychiatric symptoms and by cognitive impairment in the carereceiver. Wanting to relinquish the caring role appears to be a function of the carer's mental capacity to cope and the carereceiver's awareness of the social and physical environment.

Finally, gender failed to emerge as a significant predictor of burden. Two gender-related variables took its place in the final regression equation, having a breaking point and minor psychiatric symptoms. These findings combined with others from the demographic analyses present a somewhat different picture of gender differences in caregiving than others have portrayed. While gender was of the utmost importance in determining who cares, gender was irrelevant to the activities that primary caregivers engaged in and to the crises they experienced. There was no evidence that women who care do more or are more aware of the carereceiver's needs than men who care. Nevertheless, women were slightly more burdened than men, they reported more symptoms, they were more likely to know they had a breaking point, and they used respite care more often. This in itself does not advance our understanding of gender differences in caregiving, but two other findings help to focus an emerging picture of men and women as carers. Women expressed a stronger concern for the welfare of others and were more likely to use the coping strategy of reinterpretation and acceptance in the caregiving role. The picture emerges of women and men doing the same thing in the caregiving role, but seeing themselves very differently. Again the distinction is made between caring as doing and caring as being (Graham, 1983). For women caring is not something that just has to be done, it is an opportunity to act out the values that are central to their own identity. They want to care, but at the same time it hurts to care as they confront frustrations and sadness. They cannot make things right when the carereceiver's health is failing. To resolve their conflict women have the choice of either rejecting their nurturing values or accepting the anguish of caregiving, perhaps convincing themselves that the situation is not as bad as it seems. The women in this study opted for the latter, a coping response which proved to be ineffective, providing no relief from burden and increasing their risk of minor psychiatric symptoms. Considered together, these data suggest that the burden that women carry in caregiving and that men do not is that they care about their role too much: Their identity is bound up in something which, although having its own rewards, is painful and distressing. So many of the women in this study answered the question, 'Who will care for you in your old age?' with the words, 'I would never wish this on my children'.

## The variables which accounted for the variance

The burdened carer is one who perceives him or herself as having too little time to do things, sole responsibility for care, minor psychiatric symptoms, a breaking point in relation to future care, much to learn about caregiving, and a carereceiver with emotionally or cognitively impaired behaviour.

*Time constraints*: A set of variables excluded from the burden concept once it had been defined in terms of basic need frustration involved time constraints—foregoing outings and holidays, giving up leisure activities and interests, spending less time with the family and having little time to oneself. Such sacrifices, while undoubtedly important to many people, need not necessarily threaten well-being and occur with many roles in which adults are expected to engage responsibly and capably on a daily basis. Nevertheless, time constraints played a major role in predicting the more serious problem of caregiving burden.

*Sole responsibility*: If caregivers feel that they are the only ones who can provide care, they may put themselves under greater pressure, tolerate more frustration of basic needs than is necessary and consequently experience greater burden. In response to this interpretation, a sceptic might say that it is not surprising for a carer who is depressed or anxious to feel alone in the caregiving role, to feel they have the worries of the world on their shoulders and to feel they may not be doing things as well as they should. Undoubtedly, there is some truth in this argument. But it does not account entirely for the relationships which have emerged among the variables. Sole responsibility remained a significant predictor of burden after controlling for the mood state of the carer. At this stage, the proposition stands that perceptions of oneself as solely responsible for caregiving increases the likelihood of experiencing burden.

*Minor psychiatric symptoms*: The importance of minor psychiatric symptoms cannot be discussed without first addressing what might be called its 'wandering status'. In Chapter 2, burden was related to mental well-being by means of the arguments made by stress theorists such as Lazarus et al. (1985) and need theorists such as Maslow (1954, 1962). If threatening circumstances are not dealt with effectively or if need frustration continues unabated, poor mental health will result. According to this model, mental well-being is a consequence of level of burden; yet here we are using it as a predictor of burden.

The stress and needs models provide explanations of why symptoms appear. Such models, however, do not negate the role that symptoms may play once they have emerged and the process of caregiving continues. Within the caregiving context, it is difficult to imagine the process being anything other than circular. A carer who is depressed or anxious may regard the caring situation as more burdensome as a result—the carer may be more fearful, sleep less, not eat properly, feel distanced from loved ones, perform tasks less adequately or feel less able. These behaviours then would be expected to increase the likelihood of depression. It makes sense to think of symptoms not only as a consequence of burden but as a precursor of burden. Indeed, Poulshock and Deimling (1984) have proposed a model in which symptoms precede burden.

In order to understand the value of using symptoms as a predictor, the dual ways in which the present data can be used require clarification. One goal is to explore the nature of burden: what it is and how it can be reduced. This can be done in only a limited way with these data because of the enormous difficulties in distinguishing cause and effect. Nevertheless, such a model has guided this research and a modified version of this model will be presented later in the chapter to guide further research. A second less ambitious goal can be achieved with greater confidence using these same data. The goal is to identify a set of predictor variables—not necessarily causally linked with burden—which can be reliably used by practitioners to identify caregivers at risk. Anxiety and depression are familiar concepts in health care settings and can be readily assessed by well developed instruments of known reliability and validity. The data from this study suggest that minor psychiatric symptoms are a useful marker for identifying the burdened caregiver.

*Awareness of a breaking point and learning*: Carers able to specify a breaking point are aware of future threats from caregiving. Threat has been defined as central to the notion of burden. It is not surprising, therefore, to find that those who see greater threats ahead are those who are already being threatened by caregiving.

Having much to learn about caregiving was intended to measure how well equipped the carer was to care at home. The pattern of relationships of this variable with others, however, suggested that more was being measured than learning to deal with disability. How much had to be learnt was not as strongly related to impairment in the carereceiver as one might have expected. For instance, the variable was not related to either emotional disturbance or cognitive impairment at all. It had significant but unimpressive correlations with the workload variables, household activities and personal care. Its strongest correlates apart from burden were time constraints and awareness of a breaking point.

These relationships become more interpretable when the qualitative data on what had to be learnt was examined. A sizeable 45 per cent of carers mentioned developing a caring personality, in particular, learning to be patient. This suggests that having the right temperament or lifestyle for caregiving may be an important consideration.

Inconsistent with this argument are the personality analyses conducted in Chapter 9. No evidence could be found of a caregiving temperament. The broad personality measures which were used, however, may have been far too insensitive to pick up the personal characteristics which make caregiving more tolerable. An approach to personality which is geared specifically to the caring situation may prove more successful, or one concerned more with lifestyle than personality. Previous experience with caregiving, a leisurely pace of life and a congenial caring environment are all factors which might be examined more closely.

*Emotional and cognitive impairment*: The cognitive and emotional degeneration scales were designed to measure the loss of sufficient control to function normally in a social situation. In fact, they too measured more than was intended.

The emotional disturbance scale did not only tap the characteristics of the person receiving care, but also the quality of the relationship between caregiver and carereceiver. Autonomy, the degree to which the carereceiver had traditionally dominated the caregiver, disappeared as a predictor once emotional disturbance was entered into the equation. We cannot underestimate the social component in social degeneration.

Some would argue that carers who had never got along with the person they were caring for would harbour past resentments, exaggerate any deficiencies in behaviour which they observed, and paint their relative in the worst possible light. Undoubtedly, this behaviour has occurred in some cases. As an explanation of the findings, however, the proposition fails to take account of the complexities of intimate human relationships. To the extent that carers can feel vindictive and resentful, they also feel guilty, bereft, concerned, obligated, responsible and protective. It is unlikely that any one emotional state consistently determines the carer's assessment of the person being cared for. The 'vindictiveness argument' can be refuted on other grounds as well. The relationship between caregiver and carereceiver was associated with the assessment of emotional degeneration, not cognitive degeneration. If the carer's judgements were seriously prejudiced, reports of cognitive deterioration should have been similarly distorted.

The interpretation which deserves most attention is the notion put forward earlier that emotionally disruptive behaviour is not merely a characteristic of an individual but a function of the social environment. Langer and Rodin (1976) have convincingly demonstrated how behaviours of elderly residents in institutional settings can be modified by changes in patterns of social interaction with staff. There is no reason to suppose that the same principle is not just as applicable in home care. The notion that some interpersonal relationships optimise self-esteem and the performance of individuals while others escalate degeneration is considered to be of major importance in analysing the pros and cons of caregiving.

The quality of the relationship, however, is only the unexpected component of the emotional and cognitive impairment scale. The measure is primarily concerned with the carereceiver's capacity to function in a normal social situation. The data suggest that when caregivers perceive things like disorientation in time and space, an inability to retain a line of thought, social withdrawal, and lack of emotional control, they are far more likely to experience burden.

The findings are interpreted as providing strong support for the degeneration argument presented earlier in the book. Providing care for someone who is not getting any better is not reinforcing. To provide care to someone who can no longer interact socially at the most basic level is enormously threatening. Few would choose to end their lives as 'a vegetable' Our society provides us with few props or opportunities to adjust to dependency or degeneration in ourselves or in others. Disabled persons' outrage at being patronised and pitied and current debates over cases of euthanasia are just two examples of how we are grappling as a society to come to terms with these issues.

Magnifying this basic fear is the fact that most carers face degeneration for extended periods of time without escape, a situation which not even the most experienced intensive care nurse would be expected to endure. Furthermore, the degeneration is being observed not in a stranger but in a family member — usually a parent or a spouse. The closeness and history of the relationship makes possible the painful comparison between 'the person he once was' and 'the shell he is now'. Providing care to a person one has known for some time makes it impossible to depersonalise the situation. Witnessing degeneration thus becomes more than just another experience in the life of a carer: It becomes the most heart wrenching and haunting experience of their lives.

Degeneration threatens the life and dignity of the carereceiver. It threatens the caregiver in that it is a constant reminder of the fragility of human life. Last but not least, it threatens partnerships and friendships. Where carers are watching a loved one deteriorate, they are experiencing a personal loss and a prolonged grief. In addition, they have to accept their own helplessness. Having responsibility for care but being unable to reverse the suffering is a major dilemma which the carer of someone who has a degenerative illness must resolve. It is little wonder that such carers are at risk of burden.

## Are there no objective indicators?

For some, these findings will be disappointing. The significant predictors do not include the more measurable objective indicators which were excluded from the definition of burden in Chapter 2, but which were hypothesised as factors contributing to burden. Would those who feel uncomfortable with subjective measures have gained greater satisfaction had we relied on a larger set of more objective indicators?

One approach to answering this question lies in using a multiple linear regression model in which the objective predictors are entered first as a block, followed by the more subjective indices. The most objective measures one can find are the demographic variables (caregiver's age and gender, carereceiver's age and gender, living arrangement and the formal caring relationship). Other relatively objective measures are occupational status of the caregiver and carereceiver, years spent caring, the carer's competing commitments (marriage, children under sixteen years of age and work), and having a three-generation household. At an intermediate level on the objective–subjective continuum are variables which call on respondents to recount facts. A review of our measures yielded six such variables — three task-oriented workload measures (household activities, personal care, supervision), two provision of help measures (assistance with household activities, general assistance), and the size of the carer's social network. These in-between variables constituted the second block to be entered into the regression model.

Instead of entering the subjective indices as a third block, one of the variables was singled out for inclusion before all others — minor psychiatric symptoms. A criticism often made of research in which

**Table 11.2  The r and R² coefficients in the prediction of burden and minor psychiatric symptoms from objective, in-between and subjective predictors**

| Predictor blocks and variables | Criteria | |
|---|---|---|
| | Burden | Minor psychiatric symptoms |
| | r | r |
| **Objective block** | | |
| Caregiver's age | −.16* | −.01 |
| Carereceiver's age | −.04 | −.12 |
| Caregiver's sex | .19* | .16* |
| Carereceiver's sex | −.09 | −.23** |
| Living arrangement | −.01 | .17* |
| Spouse care | −.13 | .05 |
| Time caring | .02 | −.06 |
| Caregiver's work status | −.02 | −.09 |
| Three generation household | .17* | −.06 |
| Children under 16 | .18 | .11 |
| Non-dependent spouse | .10 | .00 |
| Caregiver's occupational status | .10 | .24** |
| Carereceiver's occupational status | −.01 | .20** |
| **R²** | 12% | 17%* |
| **In between block** | | |
| Household activities | .02 | .12 |
| Personal care | −.01 | .05 |
| Supervision | .00 | .25** |
| Assistance with household activities | −.07 | .06 |
| General assistance | −.08 | −.04 |
| Caregiver's social interaction | .10 | −.22** |
| **R²** | 14% | 24%* |
| **Subjective block I** | | |
| Minor psychiatric symptoms | .43*** | — |
| **R²** | 34% | — |
| **Subjective block II** | | |
| Sole responsibility | .43*** | — |
| Emotional and cognitive impairment | .55*** | .29*** |
| Learning about caregiving | .31*** | — |
| Time constraints | .52*** | .21** |
| Breaking point | .27*** | — |
| Carer as confidant | — | −.19* |
| Carer's health | — | −.40*** |
| **R²** | 70% | 46% |

Notes:  *  $p<.05$     **  $p<.01$     ***  $p<.001$

both predictor and criterion variables are measured through a self-report methodology is that mood may be the underlying explanatory factor. In other words, we see the world consistently through rose-coloured glasses or alternatively through a grey gloom. By entering a mood state measure, minor psychiatric symptoms, into the equation as the third block, the mood state variance can be partialled out before the remaining subjective indices are examined for their importance. The fourth step thus saw the addition of the subjective indices. Because the number of subjective indices far outnumbered the--objective, only those variables with significant beta weights in the previous analyses were entered into the equation. The subjective block comprised the emotional and cognitive impairment scale, the sole responsibility index, the time constraints scale, and the variables, learning about caring and awareness of a breaking point.

This regression analysis clearly demonstrates the importance of the subjective indices over an objective and semi-objective data base (see Table 11.2). When the objective social and demographic indicators were included in the analysis, only 12 per cent of the variance in burden could be accounted for. The semi-objective workload and social integration measures increased the proportion to 14 per cent. Mood state added a further 20 per cent. With the addition of only those subjective indices which had significant beta weights in the previous regression analysis, the variance accounted for rose a further 36 per cent. The subjective indicators are indeed important.

## Is burden the right concept?

We have found that the predictors of burden are essentially subjective. Those feeling frustrated at this point at the demise of the objective indicators could be forgiven for suggesting that the fault lies in the way burden has been defined and measured. There is clearly no right way to define a construct. However, we can and should question the usefulness of this definition and examine the advantages of the construct over other more familiar constructs.

One way of addressing this issue is through comparing the burden analyses with similar analyses using minor psychiatric symptoms as the criterion. Mental illness among caregivers is a problem well recognised among health care professionals. Furthermore, depression and anxiety are well researched constructs in clinical and general population settings. Measures of known reliability and validity are widely available. Indeed, the depression and anxiety measures used in this study had performed well psychometrically in the past in the population from which the sample was drawn (Henderson et al., 1981).

*What are the major predictors of minor psychiatric symptoms?*

The procedure followed to identify the major predictors of minor psychiatric symptoms was the same as that used with burden. The major correlates from each set of variables outlined in Table 3.1 were entered into a stepwise multiple linear regression analysis to ascertain which accounted for the maximum variance in the criterion. The variables, their correlations with minor psychiatric symptoms, and their beta weights appear in Table 11.3.

The majority of the predictors failed to emerge with significant beta weights in Model 1. Yet 53 per cent of the variance in symptoms was accounted for. Dominating the analysis was the personality measure, emotionality. Given the doubts that have already been expressed about differentiating symptom states from more enduring traits within the caregiving context, the remaining regression models were set up excluding the personality measures. Model 2 examined the remaining caregiving predictors which together accounted for 36 per cent of the variance.

The predictors which emerged with significant beta weights were the carer's health, time constraints, socio-economic status, not being

**Table 11.3    Correlations and beta weights for the regression of minor psychiatric symptoms on the major explanatory variables (N=126)**

| Major explanatory variables | r | Model 1 Beta | Model 2 Beta |
|---|---|---|---|
| Carer as confidant of carereceiver | −.19* | −.20* | −.19* |
| Carer's availability of social interaction | −.22** | ns | ns |
| Loss in carer's social interaction | .21** | ns | ns |
| Carer's health | −.40*** | −.23** | −.38*** |
| Carer's socio-economic status | .24** | ns | .18* |
| Use of carer's support group | −.20** | ns | ns |
| Emotionality of carer | .59*** | .47*** | — |
| Mastery of carer | −.50*** | ns | — |
| Sole responsibility | .20** | .17* | ns |
| Time constraints | .21** | ns | .16* |
| Knowledge about carereceiver's condition initially | −.22** | ns | ns |
| Preferred nursing home placement | .24** | ns | ns |
| Conflict with carereceiver | .19* | ns | ns |
| Quantity of supervision of carereceiver | .25** | .21** | .18* |
| Emotional and cognitive impairment scale | .29*** | .15* | .21** |
| Carereceiver's gender | −.23** | ns | ns |

Notes:    *  $p<.05$        **  $p<.01$        ***  $p<.001$

the carereceiver's confidant, supervisory demands and perceptions of emotional and cognitive impairment in the carereceiver.

Emotional and cognitive impairment in the carereceiver was an important predictor of minor psychiatric symptoms. Impairment increased the likelihood of symptoms as it did burden, but in the present analysis it dominated many of the other predictors. Having little knowledge initially and bearing sole responsibility for caregiving were beliefs which were no longer significant once measures of emotional and cognitive impairment had been entered into the equation.

Being a confidant of the carereceiver decreased the chances of mental illness in the caregiver. Once this variable and the emotional and cognitive impairment scale had been entered into the regression equation, the interpersonal conflict variable became unimportant. The quality of the relationship between caregiver and carereceiver was represented through carer as confidant and the degree of degeneration in the carereceiver.

A third significant predictor, the time constraints index, emerged in the minor psychiatric symptoms analyses as in the burden analyses. The index taps elements of both role strain and role conflict, concepts which have been linked with poor mental health in a variety of stress situations (Pearlin et al., 1981).

The relationships of mental health with both physical health and social class are not peculiar to the caregiving context and are well-documented findings. More interesting is the relationship of physical health to other predictors. Once health had been entered into the regression equation, use of a self-help support group was no longer a significant predictor. The difference between those who join self-help groups and those who do not may have more to do with their physical capacity to get there than with their state of psychological well-being.

The remaining significant predictor is the need for supervision. Why this contributed to explaining symptoms but not burden is puzzling. Initially it was hypothesised as being one of the major contributors to both burden and symptoms. In Chapter 7, the relationship with symptoms was explained as part of the loss experienced by carers watching a loved one deteriorate. These analyses do not support this interpretation. Supervisory activities correlated only very weakly with the degeneration scales. The role played by supervision in relation to burden and symptoms remains unclear.

### Predicting burden versus psychiatric symptoms

In comparing the prediction of burden and minor psychiatric symptoms, three points should be made. First, in both sets of analyses, the quality of the relationship between caregiver and carereceiver was important. If the relationship is threatened, either because the partners are not compatible or because one cannot maintain satisfactory social functioning, problems are likely to emerge for the carer.

The second and third points deal with differences. In explaining minor psychiatric symptoms, predictors emerged which are not particularly pertinent to caregiving. Social class and health, for instance, are relevant to mental health regardless of whether or not caregiving is involved. These variables are regularly included in studies of neurosis and stress, and would be expected to emerge as important predictors of mental health across a range of stressful events. Yet our interest is in understanding the stress of caregiving. Burden, in contrast to mental health, is defined in such a way that caregiving is an integral part of the concept.

The other major difference is the extent to which the major predictors dominate the mental health regression analyses. The relationship and degeneration indices made many other variables redundant in the prediction of symptoms. This was not the case in predicting burden.

The explanation for this difference may be found in the fundamental distinction between burden and symptoms. Burden represents perceptions of threat. In contrast, minor psychiatric symptoms are extreme emotional responses which carers may not be able to explain. One could argue that symptoms are a more severe manifestation of problems than burden. While many little things may cause burden, it is conceivable that only the more serious factors, and perhaps those over which carers have least control, will account for the development of symptoms. Frustrations which carers hope they can control pale into insignificance beside those which they cannot control. The relationship and degeneration variables, the dominant predictors of symptoms, represent factors which are not in the carer's control.

This comparison of the prediction of minor psychiatric symptoms and burden supports rather than undermines the usefulness of the burden construct. On the one hand, the minor psychiatric symptoms construct has the advantage of representing a more serious level of distress in the carer. On the other hand, one would hope that caregiving problems could be identified before mental health was jeopardised. Such a position, however, rests on the assumption that preventive social policies are superior to remedial social policies. On purely health grounds, such a stance is not likely to meet opposition. Consideration of economic factors, however, may lead to a more equivocal position. Economic analyses may give rise to a diversity of views on the point at which community intervention is desirable. If, under such circumstances, the more serious mental health criterion is preferred, caution is nevertheless needed in its use. One needs to be assured that poor mental health is linked with caregiving and not to extraneous factors related to physical well-being, personality, or interpersonal relationships which are not within the social welfare responsibilities of the state.

A further level at which the burden and symptom analyses can be compared involves the predictive capacity of objective rather than subjective indices. Using the same strategy as was used with burden, objective variables were entered into the equation first, followed by the semi-objective indices, and finally, the subjective measures which had significant beta weights in the prediction of minor psychiatric symptoms (see Table 11.2).

The objective factors played no greater a role in predicting minor psychiatric symptoms than they did in predicting burden (17 per cent). The semi-objective variables, however, did make a more substantial contribution in this analysis. They increased the variance accounted for to 24 per cent. Once again, however, a substantial contribution was made by the subjective indices. With their inclusion, the explained variance in minor psychiatric symptoms rose a further 22 per cent to reach 46 per cent.

It seems to be an inescapable conclusion that burden and mental illness in caregiving are complex phenomena which can be neither adequately explained nor predicted by the factors which we are best equipped to measure accurately. To favour objective indices is to allow the more measurable to drive out the relevant. We cannot avoid the measurement of subjective indices, in particular the carer's perceptions of the relationship with and performance of the carereceiver, especially in the areas of social, emotional and cognitive functioning.

## Is the subjective burden index important?

In Chapter 1, a study of caregiving burden was justified through its links with mental illness in the caregiver, elder abuse and mistreatment, and the decision to institutionalise. The question which must be addressed now is whether or not burden, as defined and measured in this study, bears any relationship to these social problems. The issue of elder mistreatment cannot be examined with these data. The relationships of burden to mental illness and to institutionalisation, however, are well within our domain of inquiry.

In Chapter 6 we saw that high burden was linked with the occurrence of minor psychiatric symptoms as predicted. By means of hierarchical regression analyses, it is possible to ascertain which factors directly affect burden, which indirectly affect symptoms through burden, which directly affect symptoms, and which mediate

**Figure 11.1    A model to explain burden and the development of symptoms**

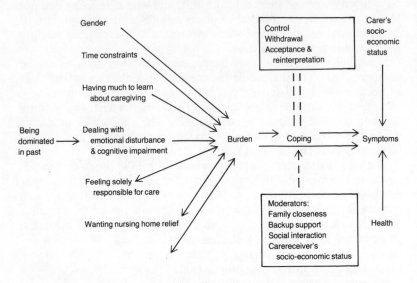

or moderate the relationship between caregiving burden and psychiatric symptoms. These findings are summarised in Figure 11.1. The caregiving risk factors do not have a direct effect on symptoms once burden has been controlled. The data are consistent with the proposition that the caregiving risk factors directly affect burden and indirectly affect symptoms through burden. Without prospective data, this model cannot be taken further as an explanation of caregiving burden. It is offered here as a starting point for future work that seeks to understand the process by which carers find that they are sacrificing their own mental well-being for the sake of caregiving.

With regard to the second issue of institutionalisation, the data once again confirmed the importance of the burden construct and demonstrated its predictive superiority over other possible indices such as minor psychiatric symptoms and personal care requirements. As will be recalled from Chapter 5, follow-up data had been gathered on caring status two years after the first interviews were conducted. Burden scores were averaged and compared for those still caring at follow-up and those who had accepted an institutional care option. Carers who had resorted to nursing home or hostel support had significantly higher burden scores two years earlier ($M=30.00$, $SD=3.57$) than carers who had continued to care ($M=27.59$, $SD=4.65$).[3] Neither minor psychiatric symptoms in the caregiver nor the personal care required by the carereceiver proved to be useful in discriminating carers who continued to provide major support from those who handed primary responsibility to someone else. Once again we find evidence of the importance of the subjective perceptions of the caregiver. Such perceptions have more to do with future care decisions than issues of mental health and workload.

## Summary

Analyses of caregiving burden have proceeded from the premise that burden is a subjective construct — the perception of the caregiver that her or his basic needs are threatened by caregiving involvement. Such perceptions of threat have been linked both with the future institutionalisation of the carereceiver and with concurrent symptoms of depression and anxiety in the caregiver. The circumstances which have been shown to contribute to the experience of burden are the carer's attitude to caregiving, preparedness for caregiving, and the nature of the social and emotional bond between caregiver and carereceiver.

Burdened carers are aware of not being able to continue indefinitely. Yet they are more likely to see themselves as the only ones who can provide the required assistance and to have made substantial sacrifices to do so. Time for holidays, leisure pursuits, social activities, family and self have been forfeited because of the commitment to caregiving. These findings point to the dangers inherent in holding up super-carers or care martyrs as role models. Striving for such goals is not in the interests of either caregiver or carereceiver in the long term. To promote the super-carer image in our society is to undermine rather than strengthen the movement toward community care and deinstitutionalisation.

Furthermore, the super-carer image may be particularly damaging to women because it offers them a super identity. Women not only do caring, they are caring. The role of caregiver is one which allows them to express values central to their identity. Yet this role brings with it frustration, pain and despair. Not only must women be counselled against enmeshing themselves in the caring role, families, community agencies and governments must resist and guard against the practice of any one person feeling solely responsible for care. Effective long-term community care objectives cannot be achieved through women adopting the super-carer role. The costs to the women, to their families and to society are too high in the long term.

Preparedness for caregiving is another factor which should be a safeguard against burden. Being prepared involves not only being knowledgeable and forewarned about the patient's medical condition, but also being aware of the impact which caregiving is likely to have on the household and its members, particularly the caregiver. Confronting the realities of caregiving and appraising honestly one's own strengths and weaknesses are as relevant to preparedness as understanding the medical condition of the carereceiver. Such self-analysis and realistic appraisal is often forgotten or avoided as distressed caregivers and carereceivers search for a diagnosis and hope that tomorrow's news will be better.

The final risk factor to emerge from this study is the degree to which the social and emotional bond between caregiver and carereceiver has broken down. The measure representing this aspect of the caregiving situation was the emotional and cognitive impairment scale, a scale which was devised to assess degeneration in the carereceiver. Data analyses with this instrument produced an unanticipated finding. Degeneration cannot be divorced from its social context. Accounts of emotionally disruptive behaviour in the carereceiver were more common in caring partnerships where the carereceiver had traditionally dominated the caregiver. This finding emphasises the multiple causes of breakdown in the caring relationship. The partnership may be threatened by losses in functioning arising from such conditions as stroke or dementia. Alternatively or additionally, the relationship may be strained because of tension which has previously existed between the provider and receiver of care, a tension which wreaks emotional havoc on both sides. The carereceiver is seen to be depressed, moody, critical, demanding or angry. The caregiver sees himself or herself as going without such basic requirements as sleep, stability and companionship, and at the same time losing any sense of competence that might have previously been had.

Altering the conditions contributing to burden is unquestionably an important goal. Some of the risk factors, however, are more amenable to control than others. Policy initiatives to change caregiving attitudes and knowledge are achievable objectives, as we shall see in the next chapter. Degeneration, however, is something which we can often do little to halt, let alone reverse.

Where the options for containing burden are limited, attention might be turned to lessening the likelihood that persistent burden will lead to minor psychiatric illness. Some people appeared to be better protected from the development of symptoms than others. Those with close family ties, with larger social networks, and those caring for someone who was from a higher socio-economic group appeared to be buffered, not from burden, but from the emergence of symptoms of anxiety and depression.

Also helpful in reducing the risk of symptoms were certain coping strategies. Problem-focused coping proved to be considerably more effective than strategies geared toward emotional control. Carers who were keen to develop a plan of action, who sought advice and enlisted the help of others were less likely to report symptoms for any given level of burden. Those carers who took the opportunity to get away from the caregiving situation also appeared to have better mental health. A weekend away, an afternoon outing, or a shopping spree are all strategies which distance the carer from caregiving and allow for rejuvenation of body and soul. In stark contrast to these approaches in their effectiveness were more passive responses which were just as widespread among caregivers—thinking that things could be worse, telling yourself that there was no alternative, or busying yourself in work. There is no evidence that such responses have any therapeutic value in the caregiving context.

Having identified a set of characteristics which place some caregivers at risk and enhance the coping capacity of others, the question arises of whether or not we can ease some of the burden which so many accept as part and parcel of the caregiving role. The final chapter is devoted to this issue.

# 12    How can we relieve burden?

Care in the community is not shared in the community. Generally, the responsibility falls on the shoulders of one family member — a spouse, a daughter or a daughter-in-law. For the most part, the role of family members in care provision has been taken for granted, and if considered at all, regarded as best left alone. The conventional wisdom has been that the family's sense of responsibility for care would be eroded if the state were seen to be offering support as well (see Frankfather et al. [1981]; Gilleard [1984b]; Land ¢ Parker [1978]; and Moroney [1986] for critiques of this tradition). Instead attention has focused on home-care services for frail or disabled persons, particularly those without informal support (Abel, 1987). The Home and Community Care Program (HACC) set up by the Australian Government is described as a 'program for people who need support in the community' with the intention of increasing 'users' control over their lives' (Department of Community Services Annual Report, 1986–1987, pp. 2–3). Mention is made of carers in relation to the Domiciliary Nursing Care Benefit, respite care services and education and training programmes. In general, however, if carers need help which is not conditional on the care-receiver's condition, they must turn to the home-care services offered in the private sector.

This is not to deny potential indirect benefits to carers from formal services. Although day centres and day hospitals were originally envisaged as having a socially integrative and, to some extent, rehabilitative function for the frail elderly, their indirect benefits to carers are now well recognised (Carter, 1981; Howe, 1983; Kinnear & Graycar, 1982). Other services directed to the frail elderly, such as Meals on Wheels and home nursing, also offer indirect support to carers by reducing their workload. And respite care, envisaged in some quarters as a service for older people without support or a carer (Australian Department of Community Services Annual Report, 1986–1987) is acknowledged in other quarters as a programme 'to allow the carer a break to take a holiday, devote more time to other family members or for any other reasons such as their own health' (Home and Community Care Programs, Department of Community Services, 1986, p. 1).

These programmes are becoming increasingly varied and flexible and the needs of carers are beginning to be recognised. Much of this development, however, has proceeded with one goal in mind—reducing the rates of institutionalisation (Abel, 1987). Carers' needs are recognised in so far as they affect the achievement of this goal. The consequence has been a poor and distorted understanding of carers' needs and the implementation of a community support programme which is not equally distributed among carers, which keeps carers bound to their caregiving role and which has disastrous effects on caregiver well-being. The central thesis of this book is that the quality of life of caregivers is an outcome worthy of equal attention in any evaluation of community care programmes, and that there is no social justice in a system which ignores this issue and indeed worsens the problem. Community care continues to function as a system in which the needs of one powerless group, the aged, are being met by sacrificing the needs of another powerless group, caregivers, predominantly women, the demands for whose unpaid labour drives them out of the remunerative work force.

## How do services fall short?

From the results reported in the previous chapter, we can identify six factors which have emerged as the major correlates of burden in caregivers. They are carer's reports of cognitive impairment and emotional disturbance in the carereceiver; carer's feelings of sole responsibility for care; carer's time constraints; carer's reports of unpreparedness; carer's awareness of a breaking point; and symptoms of anxiety and depression in the carer.

The majority of existing services might be expected to assist carers with problems of time constraints. Services such as Meals on Wheels, Home Help, home nursing, day care, day hospital, respite care and rehabilitative and independent living advisory programmes can relieve carers of duties for varying lengths of time. In the present study, carers were overwhelmingly appreciative of the services offered. The difficulties they mentioned, however, demonstrated inequities and deficiencies in service provision which prevented efficient time use from the carer's perspective.

In Chapter 7, inequities in the administration of the Meals on Wheels programme were discussed. Women who were working were expected to provide for the elderly person they were caring for. The service was restricted to male carers, who presumably could not be expected to provide meals, and older carers who had difficulty with meal preparation. Women who had asked for the service and had been refused not only were denied a time saver but were being given a strong message on what their priorities in life should have been.

Community nurses could not guarantee visiting a client by a particular time. Depending on the commitments of the carer, it could be more efficient for him or her to bathe and dress the carereceiver. Another carer was overwhelmed by the professional practices of her community nurse. 'She'd leave and I'd have all these towels to wash. She was very good with Mum, but I think she thought she was still in a hospital where you could let the laundry mount up without a care in the world.'

Day care was not compatible with the working hours of most employed carers. Those who had the funds employed people to care until they got home from work; some hoped that the carereceiver would manage until they got there; some left the office early believing that 'they understand at work'; while others looked for jobs that provided flexible working hours or part-time work. For those who were not sufficiently affluent to pay for others to care, occupational aspirations have undoubtedly suffered, income has been lost and inconvenience experienced through having to rely on this programme.

Respite care was a service which should have provided carers not only with more time but with time out from caring. Its availability was too limited and too inflexible, however, to protect carers from the strain of caregiving. Carers had to book respite care well in advance and it could not be changed as the circumstances of their lives changed. One carer was in tears at the time of her interview because a booking she had been waiting on for many months had been cancelled due to a nurses' strike. Another carer had made arrangements for respite care for her husband so that she could visit her family in Adelaide for the first time in five years. Unfortunately, she became ill and was unable to go. Having lost her respite care booking, she wasn't sure when she would have the opportunity to make the trip. For another, respite care was a rare opportunity to catch up on the many jobs that had to be done around the home. Not a word was spoken about taking time out to look after herself.

Although all these services have the potential for helping carers by freeing up their time to do other things, they do not do so fairly or effectively because the needs of the carers have not been seriously considered in the development of the programmes. Furthermore, most regular services operate between 9 am and 5 pm Monday to Friday. With the exception of respite care, after-hours services are unusual. Thus, for 40 hours a week, carers can look forward to partial relief, albeit at times over which they have little control. For the remaining 128 hours of the week, carers must manage unaided, relying on their own resources and, to a limited extent, their families.

Services which are tailored specifically to the needs of caregivers in Australia are the education and training services supported through the HACC programme and the Domiciliary Nursing Care Benefit. For carers who participated in the present study, the Carers' Support Group was the major resource along with a carers' newsletter circulated through the ACT Council on the Ageing. These services were oriented to sharing information from members and from experts. Not only did they educate carers on medical issues, financial matters and legal problems, they offered carers the opportunity of sharing their experiences, sometimes with the view to letting others know that they were not alone in the difficulties they were experiencing, other times with a view to suggesting effective coping strategies or ways to avoid the mistakes made by others. Such services addressed the issue of the unpreparedness of caregivers directly and effectively. The major problem was that only a limited proportion of the caregiving population knew of the service and could take advantage of it to the fullest degree. Those who were aware tended to be those already involved in formal support networks. Service awareness is not a problem unique to caregivers, though it is a problem which is particularly difficult to deal with because carers can become so easily isolated from the outside world. Restrictions in who could take advantage of the service, however, again reflected the way in which carers so often become the poor cousins in the domain of community care policy. Some carers were simply unable to leave the people they were caring for long enough to attend meetings and had no-one they could call on to take their place. For others, disclosure of personal difficulties in a public albeit sympathetic setting was impossible: 'I feel appalled at the thought of talking about such things in public'. Self-help groups clearly are a more viable option for some than others (Abel, 1987). This does not mean, however, that those who avoid such groups are opposed to advice and help. Carers need the option of discussing their difficulties in a private one-to-one situation.

Many of the shortcomings discussed could be overcome by the carer purchasing services privately. One immediately thinks of the Domiciliary Nursing Care Benefit as a means of enabling carers to meet their needs. Unfortunately, the $42 per fortnight is an entitlement that does little to increase the carer's options for meeting his or her needs. Private home care would cost the carer $7.80 per hour and $9.30 after 5 pm. The benefit goes only half way toward providing carers with one extra hour each afternoon to finish work, spend time with other family members, catch up on some chores, or simply to have some time to themselves. The benefit undoubtedly compensates families for the additional household expenses incurred through having an elderly person in their home and is appreciated at this level. The Domiciliary Nursing Care Benefit is too little, however, to bring relief to the burdened carer without a private income. Such carers are disproportionately women. Given that government expenditure per average bed day in nursing homes is $50.00, a little more generosity toward unpaid carers is in order. The policy in some American states such as California of allowing community care expenditure up to 95 per cent of the cost of state-supported nursing home care merits consideration. Abel (1987) points out, however, that eligibility criteria for such programmes are often so stringent that only a minority of carers receive financial remuneration.

So far we have considered the formal benefits to caregivers through services to their dependants. Such an analysis, however, fails to acknowledge the informal benefits which carers receive. In the present study, occupational therapists in charge of the day centres were seen to be major sources of information, advice and comfort. They played a major role in introducing carers to the Carers' Support Group.

The community nurses also took it upon themselves to care for the carer as well as the carereceiver. In the words of one carer, 'They saved my life'. Another carer admitted to knowing nothing about the Domiciliary Nursing Care Benefit until he had got to know the nurse who came to bath and dress his wife. Through casual conversation, the community nurse came to realise that the carer was eligible for the benefit but was not receiving it. She brought the papers for him to complete and submitted the application.

In yet another case, the emotional well-being of the carer became the primary concern of the community nurse. I arrived for one interview to find that a caregiver had just admitted her husband to hospital under very traumatic circumstances. While we were having a cup of tea, a nurse popped in on her rounds to check on the carer and make sure she was managing. She had heard of the sudden admission of the husband at the hospital. While such examples of support were impressive, they were not considered part of the normal workload of the community nurses, or at least not accorded the legitimacy of their daily rounds of baths, dressing changes and so on. The support was given at the discretion of the nurse, when and if she happened to hear about what was going on, and was fitted in around other regular duties and demands.

Thus we find that, informally at least, some carers are in contact with day centres and home nursing professionals and benefit from this association. Through such contact, the potential exists for enabling a carer to become more knowledgeable and better prepared for the caregiving role, a factor which has already been linked with lower reports of burden.

The criticism to be made, however, is that such services are not equally available to carers. For example, benefiting from the knowledge and advice passed on by the community nurses depends on the nurse's perception of her role and on the carer's availability when the nurse visits the carereceiver. The chance of picking up such information is small indeed if the carer has a part-time job on the mornings when the nurse visits.

In reviewing the services currently available, I have argued that there are benefits to carers, but that these benefits are haphazard, unequally distributed and in some cases minimal. I have not considered the possibility of carers providing increased levels of care while the state punishes them for doing so. And yet this was the perception of several of the carers interviewed in the study. Elderly couples living in their own home benefited from a housekeeping service. Once they had moved to their daughter's home, however, the service was lost. From the daughter's perspective, offers of increased assistance had been met by withdrawal of community support, a policy which does little to encourage families to care.

## Tailoring services to carers' needs

Current services have the potential for helping carers make more efficient use of their time, for allowing them to get away from the caregiving situation to recharge their batteries and for learning about caregiving. Nevertheless, serious gaps remain. First, preparedness for caregiving means having resources available at the very beginning, not after several months when carers are desperately searching for help. Counselling and advisory services should be readily available to carers and should be offered on a one-to-one basis at the time families begin to provide care. Every carer should know that they are entitled to such help should they run into difficulties at any stage. They should be told of available services and they should be warned about problems of caregiving and the need to share care whenever possible. While mindful of arguments concerning the devaluation and undermining of women's traditional skills through overvaluing the expert advice of professionals (Ehrenreich & English, 1978; Jagger, 1983; Ruddick, 1980), there was little evidence of caregiving coming naturally to the majority of carers. Carers of the frail aged probably need more support and preparation than that offered to new parents through pre-natal classes. After all, there is a domain of public knowledge about infant dependency and the transformation to adult independence. In contrast, dependency among adults is rarely discussed, being dismissed as either 'a shame' or an embarrassment.

In the present study, individual professionals such as general practitioners, social workers and psychologists were not providing caregivers with the knowledge and support many required. Not until caregivers were searching for help was contact made with them and then the support offered took the form of sympathy, services to contact and prescriptions for medication for anxiety and depression. Beckwith (1988) also noted reliance on tranquillisers as a means of relieving the stress of caregiving. While none of these responses are inappropriate courses of action, they do not exhaust the skills that these professionals have to offer. Unpaid carers have much to learn from professional carers. In some ways they are being expected to do the job of a professional 24 hours a day, 7 days a week. Through counselling programmes, carers can be exposed to alternative coping strategies, steps can be taken to relieve the pressure felt by those who have become trapped in the caring role, they can be taught to share care, and feelings of guilt and anger can at least be understood, if not overcome. For carers who are aware of a breaking point, counselling services offer an opportunity to talk about future fears, so often hidden within families, and to plan a course of action. In short, carers can be taught to maximise the amount of personal control they have in the caregiving situation, instead of feeling trapped because they have so little.

In addition, professionals can share some of their expertise in interpersonal relations. We have seen that carers who report cognitive impairment and emotional disturbance in the carereceiver are not just reporting on a medical condition but on the relationship between caregiver and carereceiver. Basic behaviour management techniques, family therapy and conflict resolution strategies could prove invaluable in an unsatisfactory caregiving situation. Such programmes have proven popular with dementia patients and their carers (Kahan et al., 1985; Haley, 1983; Zarit & Zarit, 1982). They are no less relevant for other caregivers and carereceivers who experience interpersonal difficulties (Clark & Rakowski, 1983; Pinkston & Linsk, 1984).

**To whom should care be directed?**

To make home care a viable caring option is to make a support system work. Caregivers and carereceivers are equally important in this system. To orient policies to one without carefully examining the impact on the other is poorly conceived and wasteful of limited public resources. Child welfare cases are invariably discussed and dealt with in the context of the family. The courts and the welfare agencies are most likely to regard juvenile delinquency and incest as family problems, not as individual problems. The family system is widely recognised as the appropriate unit of analysis when considering the welfare of the young (Shapiro, 1983). Similarly, the welfare of the aged person must be considered within a family context (Reifler & Eisdorfer, 1980; Reifler & Wu, 1982; Smyer, 1984; Soyer, 1972), although in practice families are sometimes forgotten (Thompson & Haran, 1985). This is hardly surprising since, at the political level, recognition of the contribution of the family is barely evident in policies oriented to aged care. The family is not the recipient of support.

That this difference exists between child care and aged care is not without justification. Children are supposed to be dependent on their family, elderly persons are not legally dependent on theirs. Independence for aged persons is not just a societal norm endorsed by younger members of modern western societies; independence is highly valued by the elderly themselves. Policies which undermine such independence fly in the face of the deeply felt and widely articulated wishes of the community (Day, 1985; Job, 1984; Kendig, 1986; Russell, 1981). Nevertheless, it is an unavoidable fact that some of us will end our lives in a state of dependency. Under such circumstances, is it really in the interests of all to continue to provide services to the individual when in the long run this may actually undermine independence through hastening institutionalisation? Might not caregivers and carereceivers be better served by the acceptance of their interdependency at the level of policy formulation?

The notion of providing support to the family caring unit rather than to one individual within the unit is exemplified by the Family Support Program in New York (Frankfather et al., 1981). This programme was based on the assumption that the state would accept responsibility for elderly persons without families, but families had to accept responsibility for care of their elderly relatives. In the event of serious disability, however, the state was prepared to provide support to the caring unit, both caregivers and carereceivers being construed as clients. Frankfather et al. (1981) have provided a detailed account of how such a model may work. The recipient, the primary caregiver and other family members meet with a programme staff member to discuss how support might best be provided. A limit is placed on how much support (in monetary terms) the programme is prepared to spend, but the form which the support takes is open to negotiation. Family members identify their needs, and staff from the Family Support Program discuss the ways in which such needs can be satisfied within the confines of the budget. Where conflict arises, staff members try to counsel the opposing parties toward consensus. The result is a negotiated service contract dependent upon 'severity of disability, agreement among family members about the help needed and their willingness to continue with their own support, and acceptance of conditions imposed by staff' (Frankfather et al., 1981, p. x).

The Family Support Program illustrates three principles of effective community care: flexibility, consumer empowerment, and the identification of the family caring unit as the recipient of support. Flexibility acknowledges the enormous variability in the difficulties experienced by those needing and providing home care. Consumer empowerment acknowledges that those closest to the situation have the keenest perception in deciding what their difficulties are and how these might best be met. Handler (1988) has defined empowerment as a person's ability to control his or her environment. Identification of the family caring unit acknowledges that care-receivers and caregivers are both worthy of empowerment and enables two powerless groups to benefit simultaneously. Those who are being cared for are empowered by a system that offers them choice of services to meet their needs. At the same time, their carers, mainly women who have been disempowered in multiple ways, are being empowered through the opportunity to make choices and get resources to improve conditions of caregiving. With negotiation and a case manager who is sensitive to both the caregiver's and carereceiver's perspective, there is no reason why both cannot be beneficiaries of this system. Handler (1988) has described the very sensitive way in which case managers encourage elderly persons to articulate their needs, to build a relationship of trust between client and professional and ultimately accept responsibility for deciding how their needs can best be met. Having two clients who do not necessarily trust each other may stretch the talents of the case manager a little more and for a little longer, but, as we shall see, the advantages in achieving such a system outweigh the extra effort required for its implementation.

Identification of the family caring unit (or in a minority of cases, a non-family caring dyad) has important implications for the way in which families respond to policy initiatives. Under a system where a disabled elderly person is cared for by the family and is receiving support from community services, the family and state are joint providers of care. Policy makers view this as the state supplementing family care; but the common fear is that the family will perceive the state's involvement as replacement care and withdraw their support. Many have argued that such fears are not warranted (Challis & Davies, 1980; Land & Parker, 1978; Rossiter & Wicks, 1982). Families generally care too much to turn their backs on their elderly relatives. Regardless of the empirical reality, the system remains one which invites abuse. The family and state are alternative carers from the family's point of view. The temptation must surely exist for the family to get whatever help they can from the state and to arrange their affairs so that the person they are caring for is entitled to services provided to individuals without families. This care delivery system sets up the state and family as rivals. The more the state provides for the disabled person, the less the family must provide and vice versa.

Under the family support model, both the caregiver and the carereceiver are the recipients of support, while the state is the provider. The family does not share responsibility for care with the state. The family has sole responsibility, but the caring unit can expect support from the state as difficulties increase, providing caring responsibilities are taken seriously. The sort of support which is given has limits, but the caring unit has some say over how their support allocation should be used. In this way, the family is given some incentive to care. As we saw previously, where support is directed to the disabled individual, families can experience a disincentive to care. Their contribution to care can mean state withdrawal. Families feel a sense of injustice when they see care resources mobilised only when other families refuse to take on the responsibilities which they have accepted. They see themselves as disadvantaged by their sense of family obligation. The earlier model gives rise to families adopting the view that the way to get support is to complain loudly, to threaten to walk out, or better still, refuse to take an ageing relative home from hospital. Is this the kind of society the welfare state should foster? It is not necessarily the case that these families do not care about their relative. They have correctly perceived these to be the most appropriate channels for obtaining help when they can give no more. The individual care system does not allow the carer legitimate alternatives. Once the unit for support incorporates both caregiver and carereceiver, however, legitimate avenues for seeking help become available to the caregiver. This is not to say the caregiver will get what he or she is seeking. The needs of the carereceiver deserve the most assiduous protection. The gain for the caregiver is the opportunity to participate in deciding how to improve and maintain the provision of home care. The state becomes the facilitator, and is no longer a competing player.

The state must be a catalyst of caring; yet we have seen that under the individualistic model of welfare rights the state can be a catalyst of non-caring. This is a more general problem of targeting individuals for welfare support on the basis of how much support they get from elsewhere. For example, we see this in the perplexing problem of poverty traps. The state wants to encourage the poor to earn a living. Yet to ensure that welfare benefits are targeted to those in greatest need, it cuts out welfare benefits as soon as earnings begin to lift the beneficiary out of poverty. This encourages the beneficiary to limit work and linger on the fringe of poverty. This is not to suggest that the solutions to this particular manifestation of the problem are the same as those to aged care. The point is simply that the model of state welfare for the individual according to formal rules to decrease support as the level of other sources of support increases always generates incentives to limit non-state help to the level permitted by the rules.

In the context of family care for the aged, two solutions to this contradiction of welfare have been proposed—targeting the caregiving unit rather than the individual, and custom-designing state help rather than allocating it according to formal rules. By adding the third element of consumer empowerment, we maximise the possibilities for a synergistic relationship between state help and family help where state intervention is tailored to foster further family help, and family help is channelled to mesh in with state services. Particularistic and consultative decision-making can render state and family help mutually reinforcing, can avoid duplication, and most importantly can avoid a game of welfare cat and mouse where each player makes a move in a way calculated to shift caring responsibilities to the other player. There is no inevitability about a welfare system which sets up a hydraulic relationship between state and family caring—as one is pushed down the other is pushed up. A synergistic relationship is possible under the three principles of flexibility, family targeting and consumer empowerment.

In this way, the widely supported and long awaited state–family caring partnership (Land & Parker, 1978; Rossiter & Wicks, 1982) can be implemented. The state is forced to acknowledge carers as collaborators in a caring programme and as precious resources themselves in need of support. To catalyse caring, the state must underwrite the carer. In even cruder economic terms, which is the currency of so much contemporary welfare policy debate, the state must protect and sustain its investment in the human capital of the carer, rather than allow the investment to run down. It is bad economics to assume that you can pass on responsibility for more and more productive activity to a unit without any new capital investment in that unit; this is an economic prescription for the collapse of the productive unit. Those who think that economic rationality is on the side of simple needs-based targeting of the carereceiver should think again.

**Conclusion**

Families and friends who provide home care for frail aged people or for those suffering a degenerative illness are themselves at risk of psychological ill health. Forms of maladjustment arising from the caregiving role have been termed burden. Specifically, burden has been used to refer to the frustration of the basic needs of the primary caregiver, needs which are physiological (e.g. sleep), or which involve security (e.g. stability and order), love (e.g. close supportive relationships) or self-esteem (e.g. satisfaction with one's performance).

The sources of burden appear to be predominantly subjective phenomena. The caregiver's perceptions of cognitive and emotional deterioration in the carereceiver, the carer's own lack of preparedness, time constraints and feelings of having sole responsibility for care have all been found to correlate with burden. Not surprisingly, burden is also strongly linked with anxiety and depression in the caregiver and with a self-perceived breaking point.

Some policy makers are likely to respond to these findings by concluding that there is nothing that the state can do to alleviate the problems of caregivers. Services cannot be delivered in response to subjective reports of burden. Such negativism, however, is only justified if one subscribes to a procedurally formal individualistic model of welfare delivery; one in which a specific individual is provided with a particular service because an unavoidably crude eligibility criterion has been met.

Using objective characteristics as an initial filter in defining the population to be targeted for state support is undoubtedly a useful strategy for restricting access to limited resources. Once such a population has been defined, however, a number of changes need to be made if governments are serious about supporting community care. Those frail and disabled persons who are without family support must be differentiated from those who are reliant primarily on their families. In a significant proportion of cases where family support is provided, the responsibility for the well-being of the frail or disabled person will have been handed over to a primary caregiver. Where a person is staying out of hostel or nursing home accommodation because of the efforts of a primary caregiver, support should be directed at the caregiving unit as a whole not just the individual who is receiving care. To be effective such support cannot be imposed on the caregiving unit as a set menu. Their needs are complex and their preferred strategies for resolving their problems will vary. Choice in forms of support is of central importance in increasing the effectiveness of the home care system. So is the right of the clients to influence the forms of support which are to be made available to them. Rather than accepting every service for which the government says they are eligible, the caregiving unit (with access to professional advice) selects the specific forms of support from a smorgasbord of offerings that will alleviate major impediments to their continuing involvement in home care. In this way the state empowers two powerless groups, the dependent aged and the female carers, providing them with an opportunity to make choices which will improve their quality of life. Of course, the success of such a scheme depends on the state being generous in the number of options it offers as part of its community care package.

In short, the task of relieving caregiving burden through policy formulation is not an impossible one. Introducing flexibility and acknowledging consumer knowledge of needs should enhance the effectiveness of community support for home care and thereby reduce burden. Redirecting a portion of community services from the individual to the family should alleviate burden through improved quality of care for the carereceiver and improved quality of life for the caregiver. In return for its investment, the state can take pride in a cost-effective welfare system which encourages rather than discourages caring and that helps supply the cement to hold families together as the basic building blocks of our social structure.

# Postscript

Occasionally it happens that one's scientific pursuits and the reality of everyday life become intertwined in a most satisfying way. At other times one confronts the other in a disturbing fashion. As I was writing the conclusion of this book, my next door neighbour lay in hospital dying of cancer. Her death was relatively quick, there was little time for family and friends to give her the painstaking care that I had seen so many times in my interviews. What made her death so poignant to me was that she herself had been a carer in every sense of the word. She had been a living example of why writing this book was so worthwhile. Here is her story.

Hazel cared for her family and her children's families with great concern and love, of which she seemed to have endless quantities. She cared for me and my family, always displaying the uncanny habit of providing just the right kind of support at the right time. And most importantly she cared for her own mother for some fifteen years; a woman whose reputation for strength and determination was legendary in the neighbourhood. Many a time Mrs H. was thought to be failing fast; but she always seemed to rally and indeed lived to the ripe old age of 86. Through all these years, through increasing disability and sickness, her daughter was there; providing food, doing the laundry, giving companionship, organising medication and providing personal care. Just before Mrs H. died, I remember visiting at what later was revealed to be a most traumatic time. Nursing homes were anathema to Mrs H. So too was leaving her own home. I remember vividly the anger in her eyes and the sadness and despair in her daughter's as they discussed the need for more professional care. Soon after, Mrs H. was placed in a nursing home. Her daughter had no difficulty finding a place; admission on the grounds of health needs was long overdue. This time, the expected death became a reality. That was just over a year ago.

Hazel hardly had time to get over her grief and settle into her new lifestyle than her own battle for life began. Cancer struck quickly and viciously. With two months of diagnosis, she was dead. As I stood in the small church packed to overflowing, I couldn't help but compare the final stages of the lives of mother and daughter. It seemed so unfair. That's not to suggest that Hazel's last days should have dragged into years. I wouldn't have wanted that for her, nor would she have wanted it. Like so many carers, Hazel had always said that she wouldn't want her children to do as she had done. The unfairness that struck me that day was that she had always given so generously of herself to so many people, but had been cheated of the time to take pleasure in the kindness of others.

Hazel, I am sure, would not have seen it this way. She gave because she wanted to, not for what she would get in return. Yet I for one wish that I had given back more. As I walked out of the church that day, I was sure that others shared my feelings.

There are many more like Hazel in the community who provide support to others, but at the end of the day appear to be given little respite from life's troubles for their kindness. It may have been their choice, they may not have any regrets. They may be happy and fulfilled. The fact remains, however, that others are the real beneficiaries of their care. As individuals, we owe them and give them our thanks. As a society, however, we have taken with little reciprocation. It is time that we did more than just accept the generosity of our carers. It is time for us to give them our respect and recognition. Social policy which acknowledges carers as much valued allies in promoting community well-being is the first step in that direction.

# Appendix 1    The affection and autonomy scales[a]

---

Affection

My . . .
1  Enjoyed talking things over with me.
2  Could make me feel better when I was upset.
3  Appeared to understand my problems and worries.
4  Was affectionate to me.
5  Did not praise me. (Reverse score)
6  Did not talk with me very much. (Reverse score)
7  Did not help me as much as I needed. (Reverse score)
8  Did not seem to understand what I needed or wanted. (Reverse score)

Autonomy

My . . .
1  Let me do those things I liked doing.
2  Liked me to make my own decisions.
3  Gave me as much freedom as I wanted.
4  Let me decide things for myself.
5  Felt I could not look after myself unless she/he was around. (Reverse score)
6  Was over-protective of me. (Reverse score)
7  Tried to make me dependent on her/him. (Reverse score)
8  Tried to control everything I did. (Reverse score)

---

a  Caregivers responded to items about the carereceiver on a four-point scale ranging from 'not at all like her/him' to 'very much like her/him'.

# Appendix 2  The personality scales

---

Self-esteem

I feel that I'm a person of worth, at least on an equal with others.
I feel that I have a number of good qualities.
I am able to do things as well as most other people.
I take a positive attitude to myself.
On the whole I am satisfied with myself.
I wish I could have more respect for myself. (Reverse score)
All in all, I'm inclined to feel that I'm a failure. (Reverse score)
I certainly feel useless at times. (Reverse score)
I feel I do not have much to be proud of. (Reverse score)
At times I think I am no good at all. (Reverse score)

Mastery

What happens to me in the future mostly depends on me.
I can do just about anything I really set my mind to do.
I feel that I have control over the direction my life is taking.
I often feel helpless in dealing with the problems of life. (Reverse score)
I have little control over the things that happen to me. (Reverse score)
There is really no way I can solve some of the problems I have. (Reverse score)

Activity

I enjoy being always on the go.
I often feel as if I'm bursting with energy.
I like to keep busy all the time.
When I do things I do them with great vigour.
I am not a particularly active person. (Reverse score)
I get worn out quickly. (Reverse score)
I have less energy than most people my age. (Reverse score)
I don't have lots of vim and vigour. (Reverse score)

## Sociability

I am very sociable.
I make friends very quickly.
I have many friends.
I usually prefer to do things alone. (Reverse score)
I tend to be shy. (Reverse score)

## Kindness

Tolerant (accepting others even though they may be different from you).
Helpful (being always ready to assist others).
Forgiving (willing to pardon others).
Generous (sharing what you have with others).

## Emotionality

I frequently get upset.
There are many things that annoy me.
I am somewhat emotional.
When displeased I let people know it right away.
I am known as hot-blooded and quick-tempered.
When I get scared I panic.
I tend to hop from interest to interest quickly.
I get bored easily.
I have trouble controlling my impulses.
I am almost always calm — nothing ever bothers me. (Reverse score)
I can tolerate frustration better than most. (Reverse score)
It takes a lot to get me mad. (Reverse score)
I yell and scream less than most people my age. (Reverse score)
I am not easily frightened. (Reverse score)
I usually have no trouble making up my mind. (Reverse score)

# Appendix 3    Alpha reliability coefficients (the diagonal), intercorrelations, means, and standard deviations for the personality scales

| Personality scales | 1 | 2 | 3 | 4 | 5 | 6 |
|---|---|---|---|---|---|---|
| 1 Self-esteem | .84 | | | | | |
| 2 Mastery | .57 | .71 | | | | |
| 3 Activity | .28 | .45 | .80 | | | |
| 4 Sociability | .32 | .23 | .35 | .69 | | |
| 5 Kindness | −.07 | .04 | .14 | .18 | .61 | |
| 6 Emotionality | −.39 | −.43 | −.27 | .00 | .28 | .83 |
| M | 40.04 | 21.57 | 27.72 | 16.57 | 13.03 | 37.50 |
| SD | 6.64 | 4.67 | 6.67 | 4.29 | 2.22 | 9.97 |
| N | 134 | 132 | 133 | 135 | 127 | 135 |

# Endnotes

**2    Caregiving burden — what the literature tells us**
1 In the field of social perception, Allport (1955) distinguished the phenomenological experience of events from objective reality. Stress theorists (Lazarus, 1966; Lazarus & Folkman, 1984; Lazarus et al., 1985) have differentiated environmental events from the appraisal which individuals make of these events. Attitude theorists have made the distinction between logic and 'psycho-logic' (Osgood, 1961).

**3    Developing a research model**
1 It is conceivable that some of these variables, particularly the resource variables, may mediate or moderate the relationship of other predictors with burden. Given the number of variables in the present model, the simpler formulation outlined in Table 3.1 was favoured as a starting point.

**4    The sample of caregivers**
1 The relatively low response rate in the Community Nursing sample was attributed largely to having to write an open letter to caregivers (in the Day Care sample, hospital staff produced personalised letters), and to our unavoidable reliance on more than 50 nurses as 'go-betweens'. While we initially met with the nurses directly to seek their cooperation, neither the delivery nor the return of letters could be closely monitored. Furthermore, follow-up enquiries by the research team were not made to the nurses directly but rather through nine area co-ordinators. The use of 'go-between' upon 'go-between', together with a depersonalised letter, undoubtedly reduced participation rates.

**5    Who cares?**
1 All differences between demographic groups noted in this chapter have been tested for statistical significance at the .05 level using chi-square tests of independence or independent t-tests.

**6    Are caregivers burdened?**
1 The inadequacy scale correlated $-.28$. ($N = 133$, $p<.001$) with carer's age. The mean for women on the inadequacy scale was 15.50 ($SD = 2.52$) compared with 14.25 ($SD = 2.44$) for men ($t(133) = 2.53$, $p<.001$). The mean for nonspouse carers on the inadequacy scale was 15.66 ($SD = 2.45$) compared with 14.48 ($SD = 2.54$) for spouse carers ($t(134) = 2.75$, $p<.01$).

**7     Caregiving workload**
1 These items formed a cohesive scale measuring the availability of a confidant for the carereceiver. The alpha reliability coefficient was .58.
2 Women had a mean of 14.66 ($SD = 6.50$) and men a mean of 12.02 ($SD = 6.88$). ($t[131] = 2.25, p<.05$).
3 Using chi-square test of independence, ($\chi^2[1] = 6.10, p<.05$).

**8     The crises of decline**
1 $\chi^2$ tests of independence produced the following values respectively: 33.54 ($1df, p<.001$), 15.91 ($1df, p<.001$), 16.17 ($1df, p<.001$), 72.63 ($1df, p<.001$).
2 The hypothesised relationships between affection and burden and affection and symptoms are non-linear and were therefore tested using the eta coefficient.
3 $t(136)=2.00, p<.05$
4 $\chi^2$ tests of independence produced the following values respectively: 4.72 ($1df, p<.05$), 24.29 ($1df, p<.001$), 6.18 ($1df, p<.001$).
5 $\chi^2(1) = 8.67, p<.01$

**9     Personal resources**
1 $t(132)=2.43, p<.05$
2 $t(124)=1.98, p<.05$
3 $\chi^2(1)=5.38, p<.05$

**10     Social and material resources**
1 Because of a significant difference in subgroup variances, separate variance estimates were used in the calculation of the $t$ statistic: $t(45) = 2.72, p<.01$.
2 $t(135)=3.01, p<.01$
3 $\chi^2(1)=6.00, p<.05$
4 $\chi^2(1)=9.25, p<.01$
5 $t(132)=3.25, p<.001$
6 $\chi^2(1)=11.37, p<.001$
7 $\chi^2(1)=4.92, p<.05$
8 $\chi^2(1)=3.98, p<.05$

**11     Predicting and understanding burden: A synthesis**
1 The emotional disturbance and cognitive impairment scales were combined because they were relatively highly intercorrelated ($r=.48, N=131, p<.001$).
2 The minor psychiatric symptoms scale was used instead of the personality scales of self-esteem and emotionality because these measures were found to be empirically indistinguishable from each other in this data set.
3 $t(79)=2.44, p<.05$

# Bibliography

Abel, E. ((1987) *Love is not enough: Family care of the frail elderly* Washington: American Public Health Association

Allport, F. H. (1955) *Theories of perception and the concept of structure* New York: Wiley

Anderson, C. R. (1977) 'Locus of control, coping behaviors and performance in a stress setting: A longitudinal study', *Journal of Applied Psychology, 62*, 446–51

Archbold, P. G. (1983) 'Impact of parent-caring on women,' *Family Relations, 32*, 39–45

Aronson, M. K., & Lipkowitz, R. (1981) 'Senile dementia, Alzheimer's type: The family and the health care delivery system', *Journal of the American Geriatrics Society, 29*, 568–71

Australian Bureau of Statistics (1982) *Handicapped Persons Australia 1981* ABS Catalogue No. 4343.0, Canberra: Australian Bureau of Statistics
_____ (1986) *Census of population and housing*

Australian Council on the Ageing and Australian Department of Community Services (1985) *Older people at home: A report of a 1981 joint survey conducted in Melbourne and Adelaide* Canberra: Australian Government Publishing Service

Ballinger, B. R. (1984) 'The effects of opening a geriatric psychiatry day hospital', *Acta Psychiatrica Scandinavica, 70*, 400–03

Baldwin, S. (1976) *Disabled children: Counting the costs* London: Disability Alliance

Ball, A. J. (1986) *Caring for an aging parent: Have I done all I can?* Buffalo, NY: Prometheus Books

Barnes, R. F., Raskind, M. A., Scott, M., & Murphy, C. (1981) 'Problems of families caring for Alzheimer patients: Use of a support group', *Journal of the American Geriatrics Society, 29*, 80–85

Beckwith, J. (1988) 'Caregiver well-being: My mother's daughter', in J. Norris (ed.), *Daughters of the elderly: Building partnerships in caregiving* pp. 65–73, Bloomington: Indiana University Press

Bedford, A., Foulds, G. A., & Sheffield, B. F. (1976) 'A new personal disturbance scale (DSSI/sAD),' *British Journal of Social and Clinical Psychology, 15* 387–94

Belle, D. (1982) 'The stress of caring: Women as providers of social support', in L. Goldberger & S. Breznitz (eds), *Handbook of Stress* pp. 496–505, New York: Free Press

Bergmann, K., Foster, E. M., Justice, A. W., & Matthews, V. (1978)

157

'Management of the demented elderly patient in the community', *British Journal of Psychiatry, 132* 441–49

Bettelheim, B. (1960) *The informed heart* New York: Free Press

Billings, A. G., & Moos, R. H. (1981) 'The role of coping responses in attenuating the impact of stressful life events', *Journal of Behavioral Medicine, 4* 139–57

—— (1984) 'Coping, stress, and social resources among adults with uni-polar depression', *Journal of Personality and Social Psychology 46,* 877–91

Blau, Z. S. (1973) *Old age in a changing society* New York: Franklin Watts

Bowlby, J. (1973) *Attachment and loss, Vol. 2. Separation* London: Hogarth Press

Bradburn, N. M. (1969) *The structure of psychological well-being* Chicago: Aldine

Braithwaite, V. A. (1986a) 'Burden in home care: reviewing its measurement and reconceptualizing the construct', (unpublished manuscript)

—— (1986b) 'The burden of home care: How is it shared?' *Supplement to Community Health Studies, 10* 7–11

—— (1987) 'The scale of emotional arousability: Bridging the gap between the neuroticism construct and its measurement' *Psychological Medicine, 17* 217–25

Braithwaite, V. A., Duncan-Jones, P., Bosly-Craft, R., & Goodchild, M. (1984) 'A psychometric investigation of the usefulness of the EASI-III Temperament Survey in the Australian general population', *Australian Journal of Psychology, 36* 85–95

Braithwaite, V. A., & Law, H. G. (1985) 'Structure of human values: Testing the adequacy of the Rokeach Value Survey', *Journal of Personality and Social Psychology, 49* 250–63

Brodaty, H., & Griffin, D. (1983) 'The management of dementia', *Modern Medicine of Australia, September* 25–32

Brody, E. (1977) *Long-term care for older people* New York: Human Sciences Press

Brody, E. M. (1978) 'The aging of the family', *The Annals of the American Academy of Political and Social Science, 438* 13–27

—— (1981) '"Women in the middle" and family help to older people', *The Gerontologist, 21* 471–80

—— (1985) 'Parent care as a normative family stress', *The Gerontologist, 25* 19–29

Brody, E. M., Johnsen, P. T., Fulcomer, M. C. & Lang, A. M. (1983) 'Women's changing roles and help to elderly parents: Attitudes of three generations of women' *Journal of Gerontology, 38* 597–607

Brody, E. M., Johnsen, P. T., & Fulcomer, M. C. (1984) 'What should adult children do for elderly parents? Opinions and preferences of three generations of women', *Journal of Gerontology, 39* 736–46

Brody, E. M., & Schoonover, C. B. (1986) 'Patterns of parent-care when adult daughters work and when they do not', *The Gerontologist, 26* 372–81

Brody, S. J., Poulshock, W. & Masciocchi, C. F. (1978) 'The family caring unit: A major consideration in the long-term support system', *The Gerontologist, 18* 556–61

Broom, L., Duncan-Jones, P., Jones, F. L., & McDonnell, P. (1977) *Investigating social mobility* Departmental Monograph, No. 1, Department of Sociology, Research School of the Social Sciences, The Australian National University

Brown, G. W., & Harris, T. (1978) *Social origins of depression: A study of psychiatric disorder in women* London: Tavistock

Burns, A., & Goodnow, J. (1979) *Children and families in Australia* Sydney: Allen & Unwin

Buss, A. H., & Plomin, R. (1975) *A temperament theory of personality development* New York: Wiley

Cannell, C. F., & Kahn, R. L. (1968) 'Interviewing', in G. Lindzey and E. Aronson (eds), *The handbook of social psychology (2nd edn)* Vol. 2, pp. 526–95, Reading, Mass.: Addison-Wesley

Cantor, M. (1983) 'Strain among care-givers: A study of experience in the United States', *The Gerontologist, 23* 597–604

⸻ (1980) 'Caring for the frail elderly: Impact on family, friends and neighbors', paper presented at the 30th Annual Scientific Meeting of the Gerontological Society of America, San Diego, California

⸻ (1979) 'Neighbors and friends: an overlooked resource in the informal support system', *Research on Aging, 1* 434–63

Carter, J. (1981) *Day services for adults: Somewhere to go* Sydney: Allen & Unwin

Cartwright, A., Hockey, L. & Anderson, J. L. (1973) *Life before death* London: Routledge

Cath, S. H. (1972) 'The geriatric patient and his family: The institutionalization of a parent—a nadir of life', *Journal of Geriatric Psychiatry, 5* 25–46

Cassel, J. (1976) 'The contribution of the social environment to host resistance', *American Journal of Epidemiology, 104* 107–23

Challis, D., & Davies, B. (1980) 'A new approach to community care for the elderly', *British Journal of Social Work, 10* 1–18

Charmaz, K. (1983) 'Loss of self: A fundamental form of suffering in the chronically ill', *Sociology of Health and Illness, 5* 168–95

Chenoweth, B., & Spencer, B. (1986) 'Dementia: The experience of family care-givers', *The Gerontologist, 26* 267–78

Chetwynd, S. J. (1983) 'Costing the role of the principal care-giver in the domiciliary care of the elderly', *Community Health Studies, VII* 146–48

Cicirelli, V. G. (1981) *Helping elderly parents: The role of adult children* Boston, Mass.: Auburn House

Clark, N., & Rakowski, W. (1983) 'Family caregivers of older adults: Improving helping skills', *The Gerontologist, 23* 637–42

Cobb, S. (1976) 'Social support as a moderator of life stress', *Psychosomatic Medicine, 38* 300–14

Cohen, S. & Wills, T. A. (1985) 'Stress, social support, and the buffering hypothesis', *Psychological Bulletin, 98* 310–57

Colletta, W. D., & Gregg, L. H. (1981) 'Adolescent mothers' vulnerability to stress', *Journal of Nervous and Mental Disease, 169* 50–54

Collopy, B. J. (1988) 'Autonomy in long term care: some crucial distinctions', *The Gerontologist, 28* 10–17

Coopersmith, S. (1967) *The antecedents of self-esteem* San Francisco: Freeman

Costa, P. T. Jr., & McCrae, R. R. (1980) 'Still stable after all these years: personality as a key to some issues in adulthood and old age', in P. B. Baltes & O. G. Brim, Jr. (eds), *Life-span development and behavior* Vol. 3, pp. 65–102, New York: Academic Press
_____ (1983) 'Contribution of personality research to an understanding of stress and aging', *Marriage and Family Review, 6* 157–73
Cox, T. (1978) *Stress* Baltimore: University Park Press
Croog, S. H., Lipson, A., & Levine, S. (1972) 'Help patterns in severe illness: The roles of kin network, non-family resources, and institutions', *Journal of Marriage and the Family, 24* 32–41
Crossman, L., London, C. & Barry, C. (1981) 'Older women caring for disabled spouses: A model for supportive services', *The Gerontologist, 21* 464–70
Crystal, S. (1982) *America's old age crisis: Public policy and the two worlds of aging* New York: Basic Books
Cutrona, C. E. (1984) 'Social support and stress in the transition to parent-hood', *Journal of Abnormal Psychology, 93* 378–90
Daniels, A. K. (1987) 'Invisible work', *Social Problems, 34* 403–15
Danish, S. J., Smyer, M. A., & Nowak, C. A. (1980) 'Developmental intervention: Enhancing life-event processes', in P. B. Baltes and O. G. Brim, Jr. (eds), *Life-span development and behavior* Vol. 3, pp. 339–66, New York: Academic Press
Day, A. T. (1985) *We can manage: Expectations about care and varieties of family support among people 75 years and over* Melbourne: Institute of Family Studies
Dean, A., & Lin, N. (1977) 'The stress-buffering role of social support', *Journal of Nervous and Mental Disease, 165* 403–17
Department of Community Services (1986) *Home and community care programs* Canberra: Australian Government Publishing Service
_____ (1987) *Annual Report 1986–1987* Canberra: Australian Government Publishing Service
Dohrenwend, B. P., & Dohrenwend, B. S. (1980) 'Psychiatric disorders and susceptibility to stress', in L. N. Robins, P. J. Clayton, & J. K. Wing (eds), *The social consequences of psychiatric illness*, pp. 183–97, New York: Brunner/Mazel
Dohrenwend, B. S., Dohrenwend, B. P., Dodson, M., & Shrout, P. E. (1984) 'Symptoms, hassles, social supports and life events: The problem of confounded measures', *Journal of Abnormal Psychology, 93* 222–30
Dunkle, R. (1985) 'Comparing the depression of elders in two types of caregiving arrangements', *Family Relations, 34* 235–40
Durkheim, E. (1951) *Suicide: A study in sociology* New York: Free Press
Ehrenreich, B., & English, D. (1978) *For her own good: 150 years of the experts' advice to women* New York: Doubleday
Ell, K. O. (1985–86) 'Coping with serious illness: On integrating constructs to enhance clinical research, assessment and intervention', *International Journal of Psychiatry in Medicine, 15* 335–36
English, H. B., & English, A. C. (1958) *A comprehensive dictionary of psychological and psychoanalytical terms* London: Longmans
Equal Opportunities Commission (1980) *The experience of caring for elderly*

*and handicapped dependants: survey report* Equal Opportunities Commission, Manchester, England

\_\_\_\_\_ (1982) *Who cares for the carers? Opportunities for those caring for the elderly and the handicapped* Equal Opportunities Commission, Manchester, England

Eysenck, H. J. & Eysenck, S. B. G. (1969) *Personality structure and measurement* San Diego, California: R. R. Knapp

Fadel-Girgis, M. (1983) 'Family support for the elderly in Egypt', *The Gerontologist, 23* 589–92

Felton, B. J., & Revenson, T. A. (1984) 'Coping with chronic illness: A study of illness controllability and the influence of coping strategies on psychological adjustment', *Journal of Consulting and Clinical Psychology, 52* 343–53

Felton, B. J., Revenson, T. A., & Hinrichsen, G. A. (1984) 'Stress and coping in the explanation of psychological adjustment among chronically ill adults', *Social Science and Medicine, 18* 889–98

Fengler, A. P. & Goodrich, N. (1979) 'Wives of elderly disabled men: The hidden patients', *The Gerontologist, 19* 175–83

Finch, J., & Groves, D. (1980) 'Community care and the family: A case for equal opportunities?' *Journal of Social Policy, 9* 487–511

\_\_\_\_\_ (1982) *A labour of love: Women, work and caring* London: Routledge & Kegan Paul

\_\_\_\_\_ (1982) 'By women for women: Caring for the frail elderly', *Women's Studies International Forum, 5* No. 5

Fiore, J., Becker, J., & Coppel, D. B. (1983) 'Social network interactions: A buffer or a stress', *American Journal of Community Psychology, 11* 423–39

Fitting, M., Rabins, P., Lucas, M. J. & Eastham, J. (1986) 'Caregivers for demented patients: A comparison of husbands and wives', *The Gerontologist, 26* 248–52

Fitting, M., Rabins, P. (1985) 'Men and women: Do they care differently?' *Generations, X* 23–6

Fleming, R., Baum, A., & Singer, J. E. (1984) 'Toward an integrative approach to the study of stress', *Journal of Personality and Social Psychology, 46* 939–49

Folkman, S. (1984) 'Personal control and stress and coping processes: A theoretical analysis', *Journal of Personality and Social Psychology, 46* 839–52

Folkman, S. & Lazarus, R. S. (1980) 'An analysis of coping in a middle-aged community sample', *Journal of Health and Social Behavior, 21* 219–39

Folkman, S., Lazarus, R. S., Gruen, R. J., & DeLongis, A. (1986) 'Appraisal, coping, health status, and psychological symptoms', *Journal of Personality and Social Psychology, 50* 571–79

Frankfather, D. L., Smith, M. J., & Caro, F. G. (1981) *Family care of the elderly: Public initiatives and private obligations* Lexington, Mass.: D. C. Health & Co

French, J. R. P., Jr., Rodgers, W., & Cobb, S. (1974) 'Adjustment as person-environment fit', in G. V. Coelho, D. A. Hamburg, &

J. E. Adams (eds), *Coping and Adaptation* pp. 316–33, New York: Basic Books

Fromm, E. (1941) *Escape from freedom* New York: Holt, Rinehart and Winston

George, L., & Gwyther, L. P. (1986) 'Care-giver well-being: A multi-dimensional examination of family caregivers of demented adults', *The Gerontologist, 26* 253–59

Gibson, D., & Allen, J. (1988) 'Parasitism and phallocentrism: A critique of social policy provision for the aged', paper presented at the Public Affairs Conference, Who pays?, Canberra

Gibson, D. M., & Rowland, D. T. (1984) 'Community vs institutional care: The case of the Australian aged', *Social Science and Medicine, 18* 997–1004

Gibson, M. J. (1984) 'Family support of the elderly mental ill: An international overview', *Australian Journal on Ageing, 3* 10–14

Gilhooly, M. L. M. (1984) 'The impact of caregiving on caregivers: Factors associated with the psychological well-being of people supporting a dementing relative in the community', *British Journal of Medical Psychology, 57* 35–44

Gilleard, C. J., Gilleard, E., Gledhill, K., & Whittick, J. (1984a) 'Caring for the elderly mentally infirm at home: A survey of the supporters', *Journal of Epidemiology and Community Health, 38* 319–25

Gilleard, C. J., Gilleard, E., & Whittick, J. E. (1984b) 'Impact of psychogeriatric day hospital care on the patient's family', *British Journal of Psychiatry, 145* 487–92

Gilleard, C. J. (1984a) 'Problems posed for supporting relatives of geriatric and psychogeriatric day patients', *Acta Psychiatrica Scandinavica, 70* 198–208

――――― (1984b) *Living with dementia: Community care of the elderly mentally infirm* London: Croom Helm

Glick, I. O., Weiss, R. E., & Parkes, C. M. (1974) *The first year of bereavement* New York: Wiley

Golden, G. (1982) *Coping with aging: Denial and avoidance in middle-aged care-givers* unpublished doctoral dissertation, University of California, Berkeley

Goldman, L. S., & Luchins, D. J. (1984) 'Depression in the spouses of demented patients', *American Journal of Psychiatry, 141* 1467–468

Golodetz, A., Evans, R., Heinritz, G. & Gibson, C. D., Jr (1969) 'The care of chronic illness: The "responsor" role', *Medical Care, 7* 385–94

Grad., J. & Sainsbury, P. (1963) 'Mental illness and the family', *The Lancet, 1* 544–47

――――― (1968) 'The effects that patients have on their families in a community care and a control psychiatric service—a two year follow-up', *British Journal of Psychiatry, 114* 265–78

Graham, H. (1983) 'Caring: A labour of love', in J. Finch & D. Groves (eds), *A labour of love: Women, work and caring* pp. 13–30, London: Routledge & Kegan Paul

Gray, L. & Lazarus, R. (1988) 'Nursing home waiting lists—Indicators of need?' *Australian Journal on Aging, 7* 31–34

Greenberg, J. N., Doth, D., Johnson, A. N., & Austin, C. (1980) *A comparative study of long term care demonstration projects: Lessons for future inquiry* Minneapolis, Minn.: Center for the Health Services Research, University of Minnesota

Greene, J. G. & Timbury, G. C. (1979) 'A geriatric psychiatry day hospital service: a five-year review', *Age and Ageing, 8* 49–53

Greene, J. G., Smith, R., Gardiner, M. & Timbury, G. C. (1982) 'Measuring behavioural disturbance of elderly demented patients in the community and its effects on relatives: A factor analytic study', *Age and Ageing, 11* 121–26

Greer, D. S. & Mor, V. (1986) 'An overview of national hospice study findings', *Journal of Chronic Disease, 39* 5–7

Gurland, B., Bennett, R., & Wilder, D. (1981) 'Re-evaluating the place of evaluation in planning for alternatives to institutional care for the elderly', *Journal of Social Issues, 37* 51–70

Gwyther, L. (1988) 'Understanding and coping with dementia', in J. Norris (ed.), *Daughters of the elderly: Building partnerships in caregiving* pp. 153–70, Bloomington: Indiana University Press

Haley, W. E. (1983) 'A family-behavioral approach to the treatment of the cognitively impaired elderly', *The Gerontologist, 23* 18–20

Handler, J. F. (1988) 'Community care for the frail elderly: a theory of empowerment', paper presented at the American Bar Foundation, October

Hellebrandt, F. A. (1980) 'Ageing among the advantaged: A new look at the stereotype of the elderly', *The Gerontologist, 20* 404–17

Henderson, A. S., Byrne, D. G., & Duncan-Jones, P. (1981) *Neurosis and the social environment* Sydney: Academic Press

Hendricks, J. & Hendricks, C. D. (1977) *Aging in mass society: Myths and realities* Cambridge, Mass.: Winthrop

Hoenig, J. & Hamilton, M. W. (1966) 'The schizophrenic patient in the community and his effect on the household', *International Journal of Social Psychiatry, 12* 165–76

Holahan, C. J. & Moos, R. H. (1985), 'Life stress and health: Personality, coping, and family support in stress resistance', *Journal of Personality and Social Psychology, 49* 739–47

Horowitz, A. & Shindelman, L. W. (1981) 'Reciprocity and affection: Past influences on current caregiving', paper presented at the 34th Annual Scientific Meeting of the Gerontological Society of America, Toronto, Canada

Horowitz, A. (1978) 'Families who care: A study of natural support systems of the elderly', paper presented at the 31st Annual Scientific Meeting of the Gerontological Society of America, Dallas, Texas

House of Representatives Standing Committee on Expenditure (1982) *In a home or at home: Accommodation and home care for the aged (McLeay Report)* Canberra: Australian Government Publishing Service

——— (1984) *In a home or at home: Accommodation and home care for the aged — A follow-up report* Canberra: Australian Government Publishing Service

House, J. S. (1981) *Work stress and social support* Reading, Mass.: Addison-Wesley

Howe, A. L. (1979) 'Family support of the aged: Some evidence and interpretation', *Australian Journal of Social Issues, 14* 259–73

—— (1981) 'From waiting list to nursing home—An unlikely move?' *Community Health Studies, 5* 234–42

—— (1983) *Day services for the elderly, Part 1: A study of day care centres in Melbourne*, occasional paper in Gerontology No. 4, National Research Institute of Gerontology and Geriatric Medicine, Melbourne

Hudson, M. F. (1986) 'Elder mistreatment: Current research', in K. A. Pillemer & R. S. Wolf (eds), *Elder abuse: Conflict in the family*, pp. 125–66, Dover, Mass.: Auburn House

Hyman, M. (1977) *The extra costs of disabled living* London: National Fund for Research into Crippling Diseases

Ingersoll-Dayton, B. & Antonucci, T. C. (1988) 'Reciprocal and non-reciprocal social support: Contrasting sides of intimate relationships', *Journal of Gerontology, 43* S65–73

Isaacs, B. (1971) 'Geriatric patients: Do their families care?' *British Medical Journal, 4* 282–86

Jagger, A. M. (1983) *Feminist politics and human nature* Totowa, N. J.: Rowman & Allanheld

Jenkins, T. S., Parham, I. A. & Jenkins, L. R. (1985) 'Alzheimer's Disease: Caregivers' perception of burden', *Journal of Applied Gerontology, 4* 40–57

Job, E. (1984) *Eighty plus: Outgrowing the myths of old age* Brisbane: University of Queensland Press

Jones, D. A. & Vetter, N. J. (1984) 'A survey of those who care for the elderly at home: Their problems and their needs', *Social Science and Medicine, 19* 511–14

Kahan, J., Kemp, B., Staples, F. R., & Brummel-Smith, K. (1985) 'Decreasing the burden in families caring for a relative with a dementing illness: A controlled study', *Journal of the American Geriatrics Society, 33* 664–70

Kahn, R. L., & Antonucci, T. C. (1980) 'Convoys over the life course: Attachment, roles, and social support', in P. B. Baltes & O. G. Brim, Jr. (eds), *Life-span development and behavior* Vol. 3, pp. 253–86, New York: Academic Press

Kalish, R. A. (1980) *An essay, in adult day care services: An introduction to the literature* AOA contract No. HEW-105-79-3008, Elm Associates

Kaplan, H. B., Robbins, C., & Martin, S. S. (1983) 'Antecedents of psychological distress in young adults: Self-rejection, deprivation of social support, and life events', *Journal of Health and Social Behavior, 24* 230–44

Kendig, H. L. (1986) 'Intergenerational exchange', in H. L, Kendig (ed.), *Ageing and families: A social networks perspective* pp. 85–109, Sydney: Allen & Unwin

Kendig, H. L., Gibson, D. M., Rowland, D. T., & Hemer, J. M. (1983) *Health, welfare and family in later life* report published by the New South Wales Council on the Ageing

Kessler, R. C., & Cleary, P. D. (1980) 'Social class and psychological distress', *American Sociological Review, 45* 63–78

Kimmel, D. (1974) *Adults and aging* New York: Wiley

Kinnear, D., & Graycar, A. (1982) *Family care of elderly people: Australian perspectives* SWRC Reports and Proceedings, No. 23. Social Welfare Research Centre, University of New South Wales, Kensington

Kleitman, N. (1963) *Sleep and wakefulness* (2nd edn) Chicago: University of Chicago Press

Kobasa, S.C. (1979) 'Stressful life events, personality, and health: An inquiry into hardiness', *Journal of Personality and Social Psychology, 37* 1–11

—— (1982) 'Commitment and coping in stress resistance among lawyers', *Journal of Personality and Social Psychology, 42* 168–77

Kobasa, S.C., Maddi, S.R., & Courington, S. (1981) 'Personality and constitution as mediators in the stress-illness relationship', *Journal of Health and Social Behavior, 22* 368–78

Kobasa, S.C.O., Maddi, S.R., Pucetti, M.C., & Zola, M.A. (1985) 'Effectiveness of hardiness, exercise and social support as resources against illness', *Journal of Psychosomatic Research, 29* 525–33

Kosberg, J.I., & Cairl, R.E. (1986) 'The cost of care index: A case management tool for screening informal care providers', *The Gerontologist, 26* 273–85

Land, H., & Parker, R. (1978) 'United Kingdom', in S.B. Kamerman & A.J. Kahn (eds), *Family policy: Government and families in fourteen countries* pp. 331–66, New York: Columbia University Press

Langer, E.J., & Rodin, J. (1976) 'Effects of choice and enhanced personal responsibility for the aged: A field experiment in an institutional setting', *Journal of Personality and Social Psychology, 34* 191–98

Larson, R. (1978) 'Thirty years of research on the subjective well-being of older Americans', *Journal of Gerontology, 33* 109–25

Lau, E.E., and Kosberg, J.I. (1979) 'Abuse of the elderly by informal caregivers', *Aging, 299* 10–15

Lazarus, R.S. (1966) *Psychological stress and the coping process* New York: McGraw-Hill

Lazarus, R.S., DeLongis, A., Folkman, S., & Gruen, R. (1985) 'Stress and adaptational outcomes: The problem of confounded measures', *American Psychologist, 40* 770–79

Lazarus, R.S. & Folkman, S. (1984) *Stress, appraisal and coping* New York: Springer

Le Grand, J. (1982) *The strategy of equality: Redistribution and the social services* London: Allen & Unwin

Levenson, H. (1981) 'Differentiating among internality, powerful others, and change', in H.M. Lefcourt (ed.), *Research with the locus of control construct (Vol. 1): Assessment methods* pp. 15–63, New York: Academic Press

Levin, E., Sinclair, I., & Gorbach, P. (1983) *The supporters of confused elderly persons at home: Extract from the main report* London: Research Unit, National Institute for Social Work

Levine, J., & Zigler, E. (1975) 'Denial and self-image in stroke, lung cancer, and heart disease patients', *Journal of Consulting and Clinical Psychology, 43* 751–57

Levine, N.B., Dastoor, D.P., & Gendron, C.E. (1983) 'Coping with dementia: a pilot study', *Journal of the American Geriatrics Society, 31* 12–18

Levitin, T. (1973) 'Values', in J. P. Robinson and P. R. Shaver (eds), *Measures of social-psychological attitudes (rev. edn)* pp. 489–502, Ann Arbor, Michigan: Survey Research Center, Institute for Social Research

Lewis, D. (1975) *Primary social networks in Canberra* MA Thesis, Department of Sociology, Faculty of Arts, The Australian National University, Canberra

Lezak, M. D. (1978) 'Living with the characterologically altered brain injured patient', *Journal of Clinical Psychiatry, 39* 592–98

Lieberman, G. L. (1978) 'Children of the elderly as natural helpers: Some demographic differences', *American Journal of Community Psychology, 6* 489–98

Litwak, E. (1960) 'Geographic mobility and extended family cohesion', *American Sociological Review, 25* 385–94

Lowenthal, M. F. (1975) 'Psychosocial variations across the adult life course: Frontiers for research and policy', *The Gerontologist, 15* 6–12

Lowenthal, M. F., & Haven, C. (1968) 'Interaction an adaptation: Intimacy as a critical variable', *American Sociological Review, 33* 20–30

Mace, N. L., & Rabins, P. V. (1981) *The 36-hour day* Baltimore: Johns Hopkins University Press

*Macquarie Dictionary* (1982) McMahons Point, NSW: Macquarie Library

Maeda, D. (1983) 'Family care in Japan', *The Gerontologist, 23* 579–83

Maslow, A. H. (1954) *Motivation and personality* New York: Harper & Brothers

———— (1962) *Toward a psychology of being* New York: Van Nostrand

McCrae, R. R. (1984) 'Situational determinants of coping responses: Loss, threat, and challenge', *Journal of Personality and Social Psychology, 46* 919–28

Mead, G. H. (1934) *Mind, self and society: From the standpoint of a social behaviorist* Chicago: University of Chicago

Mechanic, D. (1970) 'Some problems in developing a social psychology of adaptation to stress', in J. E. McGrath (ed.), *Social and psychological factors in stress* pp. 104–23, New York: Holt, Rinehart & Winston

Meier, P. (1988) 'My parents grew old right before my eyes', in J. Norris (ed.), *Daughters of the elderly: Building partnerships in caregiving* pp. 91–103 Bloomington: University of Indiana Press

Menaghan, E. (1982) 'Measuring coping effectiveness: A panel analysis of marital problems and coping efforts', *Journal of Health and Social Behavior, 23* 220–34

Miller, J. B. (1976) *Toward a new psychology of women* Boston: Beacon

Miller, W. R., & Seligman, M. E. P. (1975) 'Depression and learned helplessness in man', *Journal of Abnormal Psychology, 84* 228–38

Minichiello, V. (1986) 'Social processes in entering nursing homes', in H. L. Kendig (ed.), *Ageing and families: A social networks perspective* pp. 149–68, Sydney: Allen & Unwin

Montgomery, R. J. V., Gonyea, J. G., & Hooyman, N. R. (1985) 'Caregiving and the experience of subjective and objective burden', *Family Relations, 34* 19–26

Moroney, R. M. (1986) *Shared responsibility: Families and social policy*

New York: Aldine de Gruyter

Morycz, R. K. (1985) 'Caregiving strain and the desire to institutionalize family members with Alzheimer's Disease', *Research on Aging, 7* 329–61

Moser, C. A., & Kalton, G. (1971) *Survey methods in social investigation* (2nd edn), London: Heinemann

Mugford, S. & Kendig, H. (1986) 'Social relations: Networks and ties', in H. L. Kendig (ed.), *Ageing and families: A social networks perspective* pp. 38–59, Sydney: Allen & Unwin

Murray, H. A. (1938) *Explorations in personality* New York: Oxford University Press

Neugarten, B. L. (1965) 'Personality and patterns of aging', *Gawein, 13* 249–56

New South Wales Council on the Ageing (1957) *Dedication: a report of a survey on caring for the aged at home carried out in New South Wales, Australia*

New South Wales Department of Health (1983) *Inquiry into health services for the psychiatrically ill and developmentally disabled (Richmond Report)* Sydney: NSW Government Printing Office

New South Wales Parliament (1982) *Residential and alternate care: Task force: Final report* Sydney: New South Wales Government Printing Office

Nissel, M. (1984) 'The family costs of looking after handicapped elderly relatives', *Ageing and Society, 4* 185–204

Noelker, L. S., & Wallace, R. W. (1985) 'The organization of family care for impaired elderly', *Journal of Family Issues, 6* 23–44

Norris, J (1988) 'Notes on support and resources', in J. Norris (ed.), *Daughters of the elderly: Building partnerships in caregiving* pp. 212–19, Bloomington: Indiana University Press

O'Neill, P. (1983) *Health crisis 2000* Oxford: Alden Press

Osgood, C. E. (1961) 'An analysis of the cold war mentality', *Journal of Social Issues, 27* 12–19

Pagel, M. D., Becker, J., & Coppel, D. B. (1985) 'Loss of control, self blame, and depression: An investigation of spouse caregivers of Alzheimer's Disease patients', *Journal of Abnormal Psychology, 94* 169–82

Parker, G. B. (1978) *The bonds of depression* Sydney: Angus & Robertson

Parker, G. B., & Brown, L. B. (1982) 'Coping behaviors that mediate between life events and depression', *Archives of General Psychiatry, 39* 1386–391

Pearlin, L. I., & Schooler, C. (1978) 'The structure of coping', *Journal of Health and Social Behavior, 19* 2–21

Pearlin, L. I., Menaghan, E. G., Lieberman, M. A., & Mullan, J. T. (1981) 'The stress process', *Journal of Health and Social Behaviour, 22* 337–56

Pearson, J., Verma, S., & Nellett, C. (1988) 'Elderly psychiatric patient status and caregiver perceptions as predictors of caregiver burden', *The Gerontologist, 28* 79–83

Pedhazur, E. J. (1982) *Multiple regression in behavioral research: Explanation and prediction* (2nd edn) New York: Holt, Rinehart & Winston

Pilling, D. (1981) *The family with a handicapped child: A review of research*

London: National Children's Bureau, Highlight No 42

Pinkston, E. & Linsk, N. (1984) *Care of the elderly: A family approach* New York: Pergamon Press

Platt, S. (1985) 'Measuring the burden of psychiatric illness on the family: An evaluation of some rating scales', *Psychological Medicine, 15* 383–93

Poulshock, S. W. & Deimling, G. T. (1984) 'Families caring for elders in residence: issues in the measurement of burden', *Journal of Gerontology, 39* 230–39

Pratt, C. C., Schmall, V. L., Wright, S. & Cleland, M. (1985) 'Burden and coping strategies of caregivers to Alzheimer's patients', *Family Relations, 34* 27–33

Reifler, B. V. & Eisdorfer, C. (1980) 'A clinic for the impaired elderly and their families', *American Journal of Psychiatry, 137* 1399–403

Reifler, B. V., & Wu, S. (1982) 'Managing families of the demented elderly', *The Journal of Family Practice, 14* 1051–056

Rimmer, L. (1983) 'The economics of work and caring', in J. Finch & D. Groves (eds), *A labour of love: Women, work and caring* pp. 131–47, London: Routledge & Kegan Paul

Robinson, B. & Thurnher, M. (1979) 'Taking care of aged parents: A family cycle transition', *The Gerontologist, 19* 586–93

Robinson, B. C. (1983) 'Validation of a caregiver strain index', *Journal of Gerontology, 38* 344–48

Robinson, J. P., Athanasiou, R., & Head, K. B. (eds) (1969) *Measures of occupational attitudes and occupational characteristics* Ann Arbor, Michigan: Survey Research Center, Institute for Social Research

Robinson, J. P., & Shaver, P. R. (eds) (1973) *Measures of social psychological attitudes* (rev. edn), Ann Arbor, Michigan: Survey Research Center, Institute for Social Research

Rogers, R. R. (1981) 'On parenting one's elderly parent', in J. G. Howells (ed.), *Modern perspectives in the psychiatry of middle age* pp. 187–97, New York: Brunner-Mazel

Ronalds, C. (1989) *I'm still an individual* Canberra: Department of Community Health

Rook, K. S. (1984) 'The negative side of social interaction: Impact on psychological well-being', *Journal of Personality and Social Psychology, 46* 1097–108

Rosenberg, M. (1965) *Society and the adolescent self-image* Princeton: Princeton University Press

Rosenman, L. (1982) *Widowhood and social welfare policy in Australia* SWRC Reports and Proceedings, No. 16. Social Welfare Research Centre, University of New South Wales, Kensington

Rosenmayr, L., & Köckeis, E. (1963) 'Propositions for a sociological theory of aging and the family', *International Social Science Journal, 15* 410–26

Rossiter, C., Kinnear, D., & Graycar, A. (1984) *Family care of elderly people: 1983 survey results* SWRC Reports and Proceedings, No. 38, Social Welfare Research Centre, University of New South Wales, Kensington

Rossiter, C., & Wicks, M. (1982) *Crisis or challenge? Family care, elderly people and social policy* occasional Paper No. 8, Study Commission on the Family, London

Roth, S., & Kubal, L. (1975) 'The effects of noncontingent reinforcement on tasks of differing importance: Facilitation and learned helplessness', *Journal of Personality and Social Psychology, 32* 680–91

Rotter, J. B. (1966) 'Generalized expectancies for internal versus external control of reinforcement', *Psychological Monographs, 80* (1, Whole No. 609)

Rowland, D. T. (1979) *Internal migration in Australia* Census Monograph Series, Cat. No. 3409.0, Australian Bureau of Statistics, Canberra

_____ (1986) 'Family structure', in H. L. Kendig (ed.), *Ageing and families: A social networks perspective* pp. 17–37, Sydney: Allen & Unwin

Rowland, D. T., Kendig, H. L., & Jones, R. (1984) 'Improving coverage and efficiency in a survey of the aged', *Australian Journal on Ageing, 3* 34–38

Ruddick, S. (1980) 'Maternal thinking', *Feminist Studies, 6* 343–67

Russell, C. (1981) *The aging experience* Sydney: Allen & Unwin

Saha, L. J. (1975) 'Primary group support in crisis situations: Friends and kin in Canberra suburbs', *Australian and New Zealand Journal of Sociology, 11* 18–24

Sands, D., & Suzuki, T. (1983) 'Adult day care for Alzheimer's patients and their families', *The Gerontologist, 23* 21–23

Sanford, J. R. A. (1975) 'Tolerance of debility in elderly dependants by supporters at home: Its significance for hospital practice', *British Medical Journal, 3* 471–73

Sarton, M. (1973) *As we are now* London: Women's Press

Sax, S. (1984) *A strife of interests: Politics and policies in Australian health services* Sydney: Allen & Unwin

Schachter, S. (1959) *The psychology of affiliation: Experimental studies of the sources of gregariousness* Stanford, Cal.: Stanford University Press

Schwab, J. J., & Schwab, M. E. (1978) *Sociocultural roots of mental illness: An epidemiologic survey* New York: Plenum

Scull, A. (1985) 'Deinstitutionalization and public policy', *Social Science and Medicine*, 20 545–52

Shanas, E. & Hauser, P. M. (1974) 'Zero population growth and the family life of old people', *Journal of Social Issues, 30* 79–92

Shanas, E. (1979a) 'Social myth as hypotheses: the case of the family relations of old people', *The Gerontologist, 19* 3–9

_____ (1979b) 'The family as a social support system in old age', *The Gerontologist, 19* 169–74

Shapiro, J. (1983) 'Family reactions and coping strategies in response to the physically ill and handicapped child: A review', *Social Science and Medicine, 17* 913–31

Shinn, M., Rosario, M., Mørch, H., & Chestnut, D. E. (1984) 'Coping with job stress and burn-out in the human services', *Journal of Personality and Social Psychology, 46* 864–76

Smyer, M. A. (1984) 'Working with families of impaired elderly', *Journal of Community Psychology, 12* 323–30

Social Welfare Action Group (1982) *Prisoners of neglect: A report on the abuse of the elderly phone-in, March 6th and 7th*

Soldo, B. J. & Myllyluoma, J. (1983) 'Caregivers who live with dependent elderly', *The Gerontologist, 23* 605–11

Soyer, D. (1972) 'The geriatric patient and his family: Helping the family to live with itself', *Journal of Geriatric Psychiatry, 5* 52–65

Special Committee on Aging, United States Senate (1987) *Developments in Aging: Volume 3. The long-term care challenge* Washington: US Government Printing Office

Stephens, S. A. & Christianson, J. B. (1986) *Informal care of the elderly* Lexington, Mass: D. C. Heath

Storandt, M. (1963) 'Understanding senile dementia: a challenge for the future', *International Journal of Aging and Human Development, 16* 1–6

Strong, C. (1984) 'Stress and caring for elderly relatives: interpretations and coping strategies in an American Indian and white sample', *The Gerontologist, 24* 251–56

Stone, R., Cafferata, G. L., & Sangl, J. (1987) 'Caregivers of the frail elderly: A national profile', *The Gerontologist, 27* 616–26

Sussman, M. (1965) 'Relationships of adult children with their parents in the United States', in E. Shanas & G. Streib (eds), *Social structure and the family: Generational relations* pp. 62–92, Englewood Cliffs, NJ: Prentice Hall

Swain, C. & Harrison, J. (1979) 'The nursing home as total institution: a case study and suggestions for the aged care system', *Australian Journal of Social Issues, 14* 274–84

Terry, D. J. (1989) 'Stress, coping, and adaptation to new parenthood', unpublished manuscript

Thomas, W. I. (1951) 'The methodology of behaviour study', in E. H. Volkart (ed.), *Social behaviour and personality* pp. 70–82, Chicago: University of Chicago Press

Thompson, E. H. & Doll, W. (1982) 'The burden of families coping with the mentally ill: an invisible crisis', *Family Relations, 31* 379–88

Thompson, D. M. & Haran, D. (1985) 'Living with an amputation: the helper', *Social Science and Medicine, 20* 319–23

Tobin, S. S. & Kulys, R. (1981) 'The family in the institutionalization of the elderly', *Journal of Social Issues, 37* 145–57

Tobin, S. S., & Lieberman, M. A. (1978) *Last home for the aged* San Francisco: Jossey-Bass

Treas, J. (1977) 'Family support systems for the aged: some social and demographic considerations', *The Gerontologist, 17* 486–91

Ungerson, C. (1987) *Policy is personal: Sex, gender, and informal care* London: Tavistock

Uzoka, A. (1979) 'The myth of the nuclear family: Historical background and clinical implications', *American Psychologist, 34* 1095–106

Veiel, H. O. F. (1985) 'Dimensions of social support: A conceptual framework for research', *Social Psychiatry, 20* 156–62

Wade, D. T., & Hewer, R. L. (1983) 'Why admit stroke patients to hospital?' *The Lancet 1, Issue 8328*, pp. 807–9

Walker, A. (1982) *Community care: The family, the state and social policy* Oxford: Blackwell

—— (1983) 'Care for elderly people: A conflict between women and the state', in J. Finch & D. Groves (eds), *A labour of love: Women, work and caring*, pp. 106–28, London: Routledge & Kegan Paul

Wells, Y., & Jorm, A. F. (1987) 'Evaluation of a special nursing home unit for dementia sufferers: A randomized controlled comparison with community care', *Australian & New Zealand Journal of Psychiatry, 21* 524–31

Wenger, G. C. (1984) *The supportive network* London: Allen & Unwin

Wheatley, V. (1979) *Supporters of elderly persons with a dementing illness living in the same household* MSc Thesis, University of Surrey

Wheaton, B. (1983) 'Stress, personal coping resources, and psychiatric symptoms: An investigation of interactive models', *Journal of Health and Social Behaviour, 24* 208–29

Wright, K. G., Cairns, J. A., & Snell, M. C. (1981) *Costing care* Sheffield: University of Sheffield/Community Care

Young, C. M. (1985) 'The residential life cycle: Mortality and morbidity effects on living arrangements', in T. Hull and G. Jones (eds) *Consequences of mortality trends and differentials* pp. 101–12, Population Division, United Nations, New York

Zarit, S. H., Reever, K. E. & Bach-Peterson, J. (1980) 'Relatives of the impaired elderly: correlates of feelings of burden', *The Gerontologist, 20* 649–55

Zarit, S. H., & Zarit, J. (1982) 'Families under stress: Interventions for caregivers of senile dementia patients', *Psychotherapy: Theory, research and practice, 19* 461–71

Zarit, S. H., Todd, P. A., & Zarit, J. M. (1986) 'Subjective burden of husbands and wives as caregivers: A longitudinal study', *The Gerontologist, 26* 260–66

# Index